Facing Death

Leukaemia

The hospital lies skirted by suburbia,
leaves compete with square modernity,
cars throng transport's arteries;
their drivers have no fear
of disease
that is for others – never self.

Yesterday I baled the hay,
it was my choice to rest to work,
to celebrate the end of term,
to say goodnight to those I will miss most.
Today my body needs a bone rebore,
its active will is now controlled
by mechanics
uniformed in white.

Outside a million people throng the streets
and I am left to ponder
why fate pulled me
from this teeming crowd.

Six thirty, rounds begin.
Temperature, pills, pulse
the clink of cups, the welcome tea
that by evening drowns the palate
but breaks the monotony of routine day
where grey walls induce the eye of sleep
and merging with sterility
the clicking heels go by.
My moment of decision comes at noon
different menus state tomorrow's food
I have the choice of large or small
dull dishes with stupendous names
that try to colour each grey day
which will remain the same as yesterday,
white beds – grey walls – attenuated sound
that dulls the taste of questing mind.
I'll choose the same again
but mark the gravy with an 's' for small,
I'll wonder if the evening television show will smother
the nodding lassitude of sleep
that drugs and filtered air induce,
or whether memories of kinder days
will form a bridge
for ambition's happier dreams.

Drip, drip,
new blood replaces old;
the busy day
gives way to night,
the hospital is still,
new blood for old.
This stillness makes me whole
the mind is clear
eyes forget their ache.
In my vein a needle hangs
its red tube feeding life;
my blood is flat
its force is gone,
it waits;
while in hooded wards
donated blood
fights
the silent snake
– that is leukaemia.

'Acute leukaemia,' the doctor said.
Through these words death looked at me,
he was not keen to wield his scythe
or distant as statistics made him seem,
he had a kindly sadness in his face
for those who would be left behind,
he gave no welcome to the unseen snake
whose presence now I felt, but did not want.
'Not yet,' I cried. 'You are before your time,
we'll not make peace till hope is gone,
then I'll greet you – comforter and friend.

Now I grip the hand of life,
I grasp it tight and dancing pass you by.'

Jeremy Dewes. From: *Leukaemia and Other Poems*, 1988.

Facing Death

Conversations with Cancer Patients

Gill L. McLean RN BN (Hons)

Nurse and Bereavement Counsellor,
Hospice Kingston, Ontario, Canada

CHURCHILL LIVINGSTONE

EDINBURGH LONDON MADRID MELBOURNE NEW YORK AND TOKYO 1993

CHURCHILL LIVINGSTONE
Medical Division of Longman Group UK Limited

Distributed in the United States of America by Churchill Livingstone Inc.,
650 Avenue of the Americas, New York, N.Y. 10011,
and by associated companies, branches and representatives throughout
the world.

First published 1993

ISBN 0-443-04667-0

British Library of Cataloguing in Publication Data
A catalogue record for this book is available from the British Library.

Library of Congress Cataloging in Publication Data
A catalog record for this book is available from the Library of Congress.

For Churchill Livingstone

Publisher Mary Law
Project Editor Mairi McCubbin
Copy Editor Sukie Hunter
Production Controller Mark Sanderson
Sales Promotion Executive Hilary Brown

The
publisher's
policy is to use
**paper manufactured
from sustainable forests**

Produced by Longman Singapore Publishers (Pte) Ltd.
Printed in Singapore

Contents

Acknowledgements

I should like to take this opportunity to thank the people who have contributed to this book. In particular, I wish to convey my sincere thanks to the individuals whose stories and lives constitute this book. Without their help and co-operation the work would never have been completed.

I also wish to thank my husband, Alastair, for his support and encouragement to me over the last 5 years. Writing a book cannot be separated from family life. He has tolerated the many disruptions to our home life with remarkable equanimity.

In talking of family life, I should also like to record my gratitude to everyone who volunteered their time and energy in babysitting for my daughter, Ruth. The hours of solitude and silence they allowed me were vital. A big thank you to Marlene Loken, Brenda Gresik, Carole MacDonald, Sarah Christie, Heather Main, Carole Dickson, Cathy Carder and Ruth Ann Mortimer. Finally I wish to thank Bill McLean for his advice and expertise in Macintosh word processing.

G. L. McL.

1. *Introduction*

ILLNESS IS THE NIGHT SIDE OF LIFE, A MORE ONEROUS CITIZENSHIP. *Everyone who is born holds dual citizenship, in the kingdom of the well and in the kingdom of the sick. Although we all prefer to use only the good passport, sooner or later each of us is obliged, at least for a spell, to identify ourselves as citizens of that place. (Sontag 1988, p.3)*

Diagnosis with acute myeloid leukaemia is synonymous with citizenship in 'the night side of life'. The disease is catastrophic and demoralising. It is an illness that affects the 'whole' person and becomes a 'way of life'. Essentially, one does not have leukaemia; one is leukaemia (Cassell 1976).

Advances in medical science and technology have enabled more patients to survive leukaemia; nevertheless, the long-term prognosis for people with the disease is still uncertain and the mortality rate remains high. The treatment for leukaemia – aggressive cytotoxic chemotherapy and possible bone marrow transplantation – is unpleasant and demands strict medical control. Moreover, the pain and discomfort associated with chemotherapy are in many cases worse than the suffering caused by the disease itself, while episodes of acute, life-threatening illness demand a total dependence upon the nursing and medical staff and necessitate a fragmentation of professional responsibility. These factors effectively undermine the person's sense of autonomy, reducing his already low morale and creating a sense of worthlessness.

The diagnostic label of leukaemia provides a great deal of information about the disease process and the treatment regimes; unfortunately, it discloses little about the person with the disease and it tells nothing of the reality and meaning of his experience.

In October 1986 I began work as a staff nurse on a haematology ward. Several patients on the ward had been diagnosed as having acute myeloid leukaemia and were undergoing treatment. Curious about the effects of the disease and the person's response to illness, I started to follow a number of patients as they progressed through illness.

Over the course of several weeks, I witnessed the physical and emotional distress associated with illness, the symptoms of disease and the side-effects of treatment. I also realised the more complex psychosocial–spiritual suffering that resulted from prolonged hospital confinement, the required separation from normal life.

Each patient was unique: each brought his experience, his personality and his various means of support into the illness situation. Each responded to and coped with illness in a different way. Some chose the role of 'learned helplessness' and assumed a passive dependence on the medical and nursing staff (Seligman 1975). In contrast, others sought to establish an element of control over their illness by taking an active assertive role; they readjusted their lifestyle, demanded information and participated vigorously in care.

Whenever possible, I talked to the patients about their illness, questioning them about their experiences and their feelings. In conversation, the patients often minimised their own suffering and instead emphasised the suffering of their colleagues and their family. For example, one man, Ralph, developed a severe septicaemia after his second course of chemotherapy. His poor physical condition necessitated intensive medical treatment and constant nursing intervention. To the observer, his physical symptoms were appalling. Nevertheless, in a conversation that took place during his recovery, Ralph made the following statement:

> I haven't had much physical suffering, not bad pain, just unpleasant treatment side-effects, that's all.... My wife's had the hardest time. It's harder for her, sitting and watching. She can't do anything; she feels so helpless.

My perception of the illness experience was one of acute and total suffering. This was the antithesis of the patients' reports. Puzzled by this incongruity, I sought to understand the meaning of the patients' illness experience. To do this, I set out to examine the process of illness from the patients' perspective and to identify the ways in which they dealt with everyday conflict and learnt to live with their disease.

As the project progressed, the patients began to talk more openly. They gradually started to share their thoughts and feelings, their frustrations and their hopes. Psychological fears and anxieties are known companions of life-threatening illness; however, in addition to these stresses, I discovered that many environmental factors were also problematic. Seemingly minor issues, such as prolonged supportive intravenous therapy, the late delivery of medications and meals, night-time administration of blood and the restriction of personal activities, all caused immense distress and served to augment the person's feelings of loss and depersonalisation. Slowly the hidden meaning of illness began to emerge: it was the loss of identity and the person's subsequent struggle to re-establish his individuality.

In 1984, Nehemkis et al investigated the cancer patient's illness situation and his needs. Having interviewed staff and patients on a cancer ward, they compared the two groups and their perception of the life experiences associated with a diagnosis of cancer. They discovered that staff consistently overrated the importance of pain and underrated the importance of lost social activities. The authors described how this disparity influenced the dynamics of patient–staff interaction as well as affecting the therapeutic rationale.

My own experience on the ward confirmed these findings. On many occasions the ward staff saw the overt symptoms of illness and assumed that these physical and emotional needs were the patients' primary concerns; consequently, other more personal needs went unrecognised.

One of the main reasons for this disparity is poor communication. Several factors contribute to this: firstly, the person in hospital is often too ill to answer a lot of questions; secondly, there is little opportunity for staff to talk with former patients about their illness experiences; thirdly, the staff are often too busy to spend time simply talking to patients or they forget to enquire; fourthly, and perhaps most significantly, the staff do not ask because they do not want to know. Unable to cope with leukaemia's unpleasant nature and its potential for death, they choose not to become involved with the patient (Kriedler 1978). Unfortunately, under these circumstances, the nurse fails to comprehend the patient's experience of illness and fails to meet his illness needs. This leads to further misunderstanding and a breakdown in communication between nurse and patient. The patient's sense of loneliness and isolation grows.

The purpose of the book

Clearly, the experience and meaning of leukaemia is poorly understood, and consequently there is a need for work that can unravel and explain the illness process. The purpose of this book is to explore and investigate the lived experience and meaning of leukaemia by describing illness from the patient's perspective. In order to achieve this, the remainder of this chapter will provide an overview of the research methods used to collect the data and will explain the purpose and function of the case study. Section I examines the methods used to collect data and discusses the ethical considerations involved in studying and writing about patients with life-threatening illness. Section II addresses the nature of the vignette or pen portrait. Chapters 2–9 then comprise the personal stories of the eight participants. In conclusion, Chapter 10 discusses the meaning of the illness experience and examines the practical and educational implications of the vignette accounts. The methods of data collection and the ethical issues arising from the study are then explored and finally the limitations of the work are presented and suggestions made for future studies.

The portraits of illness provide a clinical understanding of the disease and help to identify the problems that patients face during the period of illness. This insight assists the nurse in recognising and developing ways of encouraging and facilitating the patient's means of coping with illness by mobilising the resources that are available to him and that are appropriate to his needs. This knowledge of the illness experience may also be of interest to other health-care workers involved in the care of patients with life-threatening illness. Furthermore, leukaemic patients and their families may also benefit from the work. Certainly, some details in the vignettes may speak in a way to people with leukaemia that they may not to other readers. They may make them relive special events in their illness career. For those who are in the process of undergoing treatment, the book may help them to come to terms with their own situation and gather their resources to fight the disease. Finally, for some it may simply come as a consolation to read of others who have gone through the experience.

Section I: The study outline

This book is an offshoot of an earlier research project. The original work was a qualitative research study that explored and described the illness experience of a group of adult patients with acute myeloid leukaemia (McLean 1992). Using a grounded theory approach, a theoretical explanation was generated from the personal accounts of the participants involved in the study (Glaser & Strauss 1967, 1968). The findings were presented in the form of an illness trajectory. Although this book bears little resemblance to the original research report, the study design and the method of data collection are taken from the existing work.

The study design

In order to understand human behaviour, the behaviour must be examined in context. Consequently, to understand the meaning of leukaemia and to capture the illness process, data collection had to occur within the appropriate settings of the hospital ward, the outpatient clinic/day unit and the home.

Setting

The study was performed at a university teaching hospital (850 beds) situated in a large urban area. The hospital served as a regional centre and patients were therefore referred to it from a wide surrounding area. The haematology unit, with its facilities for inpatient acute care (14 beds), bone marrow transplantation and outpatient consultation, was the setting for the study.

When individuals were diagnosed as having leukaemia or their disease relapsed, they were admitted to hospital for induction chemotherapy. Having achieved remission, they received consolidation chemotherapy and then follow-up maintenance chemotherapy.

The patients were hospitalised while receiving treatment (4–5 days on average); however, in between courses of treatment and when in remission they were discharged home to convalesce. Subsequently, unless complications arose, they were seen on an outpatient basis for routine investigations and the administration of maintenance chemotherapy or supportive transfusions.

Unfortunately, infection and other haematological complications are common after cytotoxic chemotherapy. In the event of complications, patients were readmitted to hospital for supportive therapy and care.

If patients responded successfully to chemotherapy and also fulfilled the clinical criteria for transplantation, they received a bone marrow transplant. The initial preparations were performed on the haematology ward; then, immediately prior to the transplant, total body irradiation was performed at the local radiotherapy unit. Upon completion of this treatment, the patients were transferred back to the transplant unit, where they received ablative chemotherapy. Following the transplant, the patients remained in protective isolation until their marrow function returned and they were eligible for discharge. In the absence of complications, their follow-up care was performed on an outpatient basis.

Sample

In order to examine the experience of acute myeloid leukaemia, I selected 12 individuals who had been diagnosed as having the disease. The participants were classified according to the status of their disease and treatment.

Class I   Recent diagnosis, receiving induction chemotherapy

Class II   Long-standing diagnosis, recovering from bone marrow transplantation after successful treatment with chemotherapy

Class III   Recent relapse of disease, receiving induction/palliative chemotherapy

The participants in classes I and III were selected after discussion with the senior ward staff. Those in class II were contacted at the recommendation of the ward sister or clinic staff or following the nomination of an existing participant.

Following the initial meeting, I assessed each participant regarding his suitability for the study. Each was judged according to his knowledge of the disease, the quality of his relationship with me and his willingness and ability to articulate his experiences.

The participants

The participants were approached individually regarding their inclusion in the project. Individuals in classes I and III were contacted during the second week of their hospital admission (the time delay allowed them to overcome the profound initial shock of their diagnosis or relapse) and were then followed throughout their illness. During periods of hospitalisation, the participants were seen informally on the ward. Then, after their discharge, they were interviewed in the clinic/day unit or in their home. Initially, the people in class II were seen in the clinic. Later they were interviewed at home or in the clinic.

Eight of the original 12 participants were selected for inclusion in this book. A brief description of these eight individuals is presented here:

Ron, 52 years old, was married and lived with his wife Gwen and two daughters. His three sons lived and worked abroad. In 1980, Ron developed severe rheumatoid arthritis, and this forced him to take early retirement from his job in the steelworks. 5 years later, he was diagnosed as having AML. 6 months after an apparently successful bone marrow rescue, Ron's disease relapsed and he was recommenced on chemotherapy (Class III).

Dorothy, 61 years old, was married and lived with her husband, Tom, a retired architect. They had two sons, Kenneth and Michael, who were both married and had children. AML was diagnosed in May 1987 (Class I).

Dave, 45 years old, was married with five children, aged 11–25 years. Dave owned and managed a large nursery. He was diagnosed as having AML in March 1987 (Class I).

Alan, 20 years old, was single and lived at home with his mother and brother. He worked as a labourer in the construction industry. AML was diagnosed in 1985. Having gained remission, Alan received a bone marrow rescue (Class II).

Jeremy, 48 years old, was married with four children, three girls and a boy. A former agricultural lecturer, Jeremy now worked as a social worker for the blind and ran a smallholding in his spare time; his wife, Janet, was a mathematics teacher. AML was diagnosed in June 1985. After eight courses of chemotherapy, Jeremy was given a bone marrow rescue (Class II).

7

Richard, 25 years old, was single and had chosen a career in banking. After he was diagnosed as having AML in September 1985, he returned home to live with his parents and younger sister. His younger brother was away at college (Class II).

Bill, 53 years old, was married with three children, aged 12–25 years. A few years prior to his diagnosis, Bill had taken early retirement from his job as a panel beater due to ill-health. AML was diagnosed in January 1987 (Class I).

Anne, 35 years old, was married with two children, aged 15 and 9 years. The younger child, Christopher, had a congenital heart defect and, during the winter months, he required frequent hospitalisation. Anne was diagnosed as having AML in September 1986. After gaining remission, she received a donor transplant (Class II).

Ethical considerations

Like other forms of life-threatening illness, leukaemia is a sensitive topic. The onset of the disease is considered to be an overwhelming personal experience. It evokes an intense emotional response in the patients themselves and in those connected with them. Consequently, if patients with leukaemia are used as research participants, there are numerous ethical issues to be considered, such as the right to privacy, confidentiality, informed consent, achieving accurate portrayal and the inclusion and exclusion of information (Munhall 1988). In addition, the fieldwork activities' impact upon the researcher, and, therefore, the ethical considerations, must account for the effect of the research upon both the researcher and the participants.

Before commencing the data collection, I needed to gain ethical approval. I therefore submitted a research proposal to the Area Ethical Review Committee and in January 1987 the committee granted permission for the study to proceed. In order to gain access to the clinical area, I approached the hospital administration and then contacted the medical consultant and the sister in charge of the haematology ward by letter.

The medical consultant was concerned that the field methods might interfere with the patients' hospital treatment and care and consequently restricted my access to the patients. He stipulated that interviews were not to be performed on the ward (I was allowed to talk informally with the participants when on duty) and instead, the participants were to be interviewed in the outpatient clinic/day unit or in their own home.

Informed consent

To comply with the conditions put forward by the Area Ethical Review Committee, I obtained informed consent from each participant. The prospective participants were given a verbal overview of the project. They were told the purpose of the work and the study's benefit for future patients. Throughout the discussion, they were encouraged to ask questions regarding the research project. The various means of data collection were then discussed. The interview format was described and the participants were told that they would be interviewed periodically during the course of their illness. They were provided with a set of interview guidelines and an introductory letter. The participants were also informed of their right to resist questioning and their liberty to withdraw from the project at any time. It was stressed that all interview material would be confidential and that pseudonyms were to be used in the written report. Finally, individuals were told that a copy of the report would be available in the hospital library upon the completion of the project, and they were encouraged to read it.

Entering the field

In order to understand another person's behaviour, one must learn about his world and his concept of self. To achieve this one must take the role of the other person and understand the world from his perspective.

To fulfil these requirements, I applied for a staff position on the haematology unit. In October 1986, I began work as a staff nurse (night duty) on the haematology ward. Nights off were used to attend the outpatient clinic or day unit and to visit participants in their own homes. The field work continued until December 1987.

Early months on the unit provided me with a growing awareness of the illness setting. I learnt the rules and norms of hospital life and gained an insight into the patients' beliefs, the meaning behind their activities. A knowledge of the ward management and familiarity with the haematology jargon also helped me to establish my credibility with both the ward staff and the participants (Melia 1982).

Credibility as a nurse together with the prolonged nurse–patient contact promoted trust. This trust facilitated the development of close relationships. In this regard, the long hours of night duty were particularly valuable, as night-time conversations promoted a depth of sharing unequalled in many of the formal daytime interviews.

Over time, the project changed and developed and hidden aspects of the work emerged (Archibald 1986). Moreover, my prolonged interaction with the participants led to intimacy and involvement. To maintain ethical credibility, I had to renegotiate consent throughout the course of fieldwork. This procedure is called 'process consenting' (Munhall 1988, p.161).

The continual process of informing and asking permission allowed me to establish the necessary trust to go on further in an ethical manner. The process also enabled me to address two potential problems associated with my dual role as nurse-researcher. Firstly, some people have difficulty in distinguishing between the two roles of nurse and researcher; consequently, they respond to the more familiar 'nurse' role (Archibald 1986). Process consenting enabled me to keep reminding the participants of my 'other' role. Secondly, some people might be coerced into taking part in a study because they are so grateful for the care they have received (Beck 1984). Certainly, I had little difficulty in obtaining volunteers for this project and, therefore, process consenting was important in that it reminded the participants of their right to withdraw from the project at any time.

Data collection

In an effort to overcome the natural bias that results from a single method of data collection, I used a combination of field methods. Furthermore, the diverse slices of data helped to add a richness and reality to the personal accounts of illness. The study data was collected using a combination of in-depth interviews, participant observation and informal interviews, and document analysis. The data collection extended over the 14 months of fieldwork.

Formal interviews

Formal guided interviews were conducted with all of the participants. The interviews were tape-recorded and additional observations and impressions were recorded in the field notes. The location for the interviews varied. If the participant lived within 10 miles of the hospital, he was interviewed at home during a period of convalescence. In contrast, a participant who lived more than 10 miles from the hospital was seen at the hospital. The interview date was arranged so that it coincided with the person's attendance at outpatient clinic. Depending on the ward and clinic schedules, the interviews were performed either in the ward sister's office or in a vacant consulting room in the day unit/clinic.

The interview appointments were open and flexible to allow for the person's labile physical and emotional condition and to accommodate any sudden change in treatment. During each interview, I used my best judgment to assess the condition and needs of each participant. The factors taken into consideration included the participant's response to interview, his life circumstances and stage of illness.

The interviews were conceived as open-ended. Their aim was to allow the participants to describe the details of their experiences in their own words and, therefore, I adopted an informal, conversational style. In order to initiate conversation, I used an opening phrase, such as, 'Could you tell me about yourself and your illness since the time of your diagnosis?' In subsequent meetings the opening phrase was altered to, 'Tell me what's been happening to you since we last met.'

The format of the interviews was based loosely on the interview guidelines. These guidelines were originally developed as an agenda for the illness briefs and, rather than containing exact questions, they focussed on certain themes. Their aim was to assist those participants who were writing an account of their illness experiences.

The participants were told that the questions were not obligatory, neither were they limited to them; nevertheless, all the participants adhered closely to the agenda in their accounts. Moreover, when three of these participants were interviewed later in the study, each requested that the guideline topics be used as a framework for discussion. As a result of this experience, the written guidelines were implemented as a basis for all the formal interviews.

Personal biographical data (family life, job, interests and hobbies) was obtained during the introductory interviews. Initially, this was thought to be dross material and efforts were made to eliminate it. Subsequently, however, this information provided insight into the participants' coping behaviour and the personal resources that were available to them.

The initial interviews tended to be superficial but, as the project progressed, the conversations deepened and became more intimate. In addition, my interview technique also improved, allowing the participants to explore and share their thoughts and emotions more freely.

Kvale (1983, p.179) warns, 'It is often difficult to terminate a qualitative interview.' Accordingly, the duration of the formal taped interviews ranged from 20–90 minutes. Many of the longer conversations then continued for a further 1–2 hours beyond the end of the tape. In an effort to capture the content of these informal conversations, field notes and quotes were written up at the end of each interview.

The interviews were tape-recorded and transcribed verbatim. Tapes were then replayed in order to clarify queries and acquire 'a feeling' for them. Significant pauses or vocal inflections suggestive of emotion were marked on the script for future reference.

Informal interviews

A few hours of formal conversation cannot illuminate all corners of a complex situation. Consequently, I made some effort to observe the participants' lives outside the ward. This involved meetings in the outpatient clinic and in the patients' own homes. Nevertheless, despite these efforts, the interviews are still narrow and cannot hope to include all facets of the illness experience.

Informal interviews took place during the periods of participant observation on both the ward and in the clinic/day unit. These unexpected conversations helped to reveal the tension and some of the problems that patients encounter in the hospital setting. This insight into the experience of leukaemia helped to clarify the meaning that patients attribute to certain situations. For instance, Dorothy was deeply disturbed by an encounter she had with a young houseman one afternoon. Later that night, she shared her perception of the incident with me. As she described her feelings of fear, anxiety and grief, she opened a window into her world (Merleau Ponty 1964). The informal conversations that occurred in the clinic, on the ward or during telephone conversations were not tape-recorded; instead, they were written up as field notes or field quotes at the earliest convenient opportunity.

Field notes and quotes

In the course of data collection, I used field notes to record the interview data together with my observations and reactions to the ongoing research. Following an interview or a period of participant observation, I wrote field notes; these included a description of the physical setting and comments about the participants themselves. Circumstantial events, together with my reactions, subjective impressions and feelings regarding the specific encounters, were recorded in a personal log.

Supplementary methods of data collection

Long-term illness effects change over an extended period of time and across various situations. Illness research must, therefore, include a retrospective review and analysis of historic events in order to determine their influence on the current situation.

A number of documents were used as supplementary sources of data. The complete list of documents is as follows: retrospective briefs of the illness experience, diary accounts, poems, personal letters, medical notes, nursing Kardex reports and treatment charts (medication charts, dietary intake).

Diary records and illness briefs

Two of the participants kept a diary during their illness. Initially, these were simple chronological records of the illness experience; however, as illness progressed, the diaries took on a more therapeutic role. The participants discovered that the act of writing facilitated a cathartic release of tension and enabled them to clarify their thoughts and feelings. Consequently, when Richard submitted his diary, he qualified its content by saying, 'It's like the last minute jottings of passengers on a doomed aircraft. Just before the plane crashes, they start to scribble their thoughts onto the back of an envelope....'

Using the interview guidelines, two participants completed a retrospective brief of their illness experience. Similar to the diary records, these written accounts served a therapeutic function; indeed Jeremy found that writing about his illness experience was more helpful than talking about it in an interview. His reasoning was simple. Free from the emotional pressures of talking, he was able to analyse his feelings as he wrote. He could work out his ideas as he wrote and, therefore, he was able to answer questions clearly and coherently.

6 months after the formal data collection had been completed, I contacted five surviving participants. I did this in order to obtain additional biographical data and to ascertain the participants' 'retrospective' thoughts regarding their illness.

Clinical documents

Field & Morse (1985) advocate the use of official documents to support and validate the qualitative data. Clinical case notes and nursing Kardex reports, obtained through the co-operation of ward and clinic staff, were reviewed throughout the study. Notes were transcribed and placed alongside the existing field notes; and in this way I was able to monitor the clinical condition (details of drug therapy, nutritional needs and nursing care) and the social situation of each participant.

Terminating relationships

In December 1987, I moved to America. During the 18 months of data collection, I had established a close personal relationship with several of the participants and their family members and, consequently, withdrawal from the field was painful. In order to maintain contact with the participants, I continued to communicate with them by airmail letter. In addition, I wrote to the spouse of each participant who had died during the course of the investigation and asked if he or she would like a copy of the interview material. The tapes were forwarded as appropriate.

Writing and ethical dilemmas

Writing this book has exposed significant ethical challenges. Although the main purpose of the text is to examine and share the participants' experience of illness, this results in a conflict between the participant's right to privacy and the reader's right to know (Cassell 1980).

To overcome the problem, I have endeavoured to maintain the participants' anonymity. In an attempt to conceal the identity of the participants and their families, I have used pseudonyms and have distorted non-relevant case material.

Unfortunately, in a small social system like a haematology unit, these strategies provide only a superficial protection. Consequently, prior to publication I wrote to each of the participants and their families, requesting permission to make their stories public. Four of them replied, granting me permission to publish. As I received no reply from the remaining four, I initiated further changes to the vignettes, thereby ensuring the privacy and anonymity of those concerned. Nevertheless, perhaps the most critical ethical obligation I faced as a writer was to describe the experiences of the participants in the most truthful way possible (Munhall 1988). Accordingly, I hope that the personal accounts that follow describe the experiences of acute myeloid leukaemia accurately and honestly.

Personal bias

With any case history account, a degree of exploitation is inevitable. This book is no exception. My perceptions, beliefs, values and abilities are bound to have influenced not only the final commentary, but also the collection, collation and final write-up of the data. Moreover, my presence and involvement in the participants' lives will have affected their response to illness.

Early on in the study, I realised that to understand another person's world, I first had to understand my own mind set, my own preconceptions, values and beliefs (Hutchinson 1986). Without this self-awareness, I recognised that I would not be able to distinguish the participants' social reality from my own view of the situation and, subsequently, the analysis and final written account would reflect my own perception of the situation rather than the participants' views (Melia 1982). To overcome this problem, I have tried to acknowledge my beliefs and values in the written report. Hopefully, this exposure allows the reader an explicit understanding of the nature of my relationship with the participants.

As the study progressed, I became deeply involved with the participants and their families. Although this tendency to 'go native' enhanced my understanding of the participants' illness experience, it also jeopardised the meaningful interpretation of the data (Cassell 1980). Consequently, I found it necessary to examine my ongoing reaction to the research environment by exploring my involvement with the participants, my understanding of their experiences and my influence on the research project. For this purpose, I kept a diary. This acted as a log for field notes (a means of keeping track of patients on the unit, those approached for interview, their response and some contextual information about the rooms, the activities of the patients), and a means for recording 'personal reflections' (Drew 1989). These records facilitated my growing understanding of the participants' situation and their desire 'to be normal' and 'to be treated as normal.' This insight influenced my approach to the participants and guided the subsequent construction and write-up of the vignettes.

Despite my attempts to portray the participants' experience of illness accurately and honestly, I realised that the final accounts would, nevertheless, contain an element of bias. To establish the accuracy and the validity of the vignettes, I therefore returned two of the accounts to the respective participants and asked for their comments. In a letter, Jeremy responded as follows: 'You have captured a very honest account of how I felt at the time. It is what may be termed source material and as such can never be repeated....' He went on, 'Due to your verbatim recording, it takes me straight back to those times.' Similarly, Richard acknowledged the authenticity of his vignette. He remarked, 'I didn't realise how much talking I had done.' The portraits were also discussed with several people who were not connected to the study. One woman said, 'I really felt I knew the man and what he was going through.' Another commented, 'I became so interested in the people that I wanted to know more about them.'

Section II: The vignettes

The Concise Oxford Dictionary (1977) defines a vignette as follows: 'Vignette: A photograph or portrait showing only head and shoulders with the background gradually shaded off, a character sketch, short description....'

The eight individuals portrayed in Chapters 2–9 discussed, explored and wrote about their thoughts, emotions and experiences pertaining to illness with acute myeloid leukaemia. The accounts are written in a style that reflects the individual's character and vocabulary and articulates his impressions and feelings. Although some editing was imposed to facilitate comprehension of the script, large sections of dialogue were recorded verbatim. For, as Thomas Cottle explains,

> *As long as I used fragments of speech and worried about what their words meant, the individuals remained newspaper photographs, post-cards, something to be regarded as an illustration, but not people to be taken seriously in and of themselves (Cottle 1974, p.164-165).*

Hoping to recreate the atmosphere of the interview and create in the reader a feeling of being there, the vignettes are composed largely from the interview transcripts. Diary material, extracts from personal briefs and letters and jottings from the field notes are incorporated into the text where appropriate. The text is written in the first person.

A brief biography is included at the beginning of each vignette. This information articulates an understanding of the disease and the individual's reaction to it while maintaining the anonymity of the individual and his family. In compiling the vignettes, I made no attempt to analyse or compare the participants and their response to illness. I believe that the process of comparison would not provide additional insight into the illness process and would in fact mask the feelings, knowledge, experiences and identity of the participants themselves.

Finally, the aim of this book is to realise a valid and authentic understanding of illness by learning the personal stories of eight individuals with leukaemia. It is hoped that the remainder of this text will help to reveal leukaemia for what it is – an illness that is part of the human condition and that has a potential for personal growth.

References

Archibald PG 1986 Ethical issues in qualitative research. In: Chernitz WC, Swanson JM (ed) From practice to grounded theory. Addison Wesley, Menlo Park, CA, ch. 13

Beck CT 1984 Subject mortality: is it inevitable? Western Journal of Nursing Research 6 (3): 331–339

Cassell EJ 1976 The healer's art. Lippincott, New York

Cassell J 1980 Principles for conducting fieldwork. American Anthropologist 82: 28–41

Cottle TJ 1974 Black children white dreams. Houghton Mifflin, Boston

Field PA, Morse JM 1985 Nursing research: the application of qualitative approaches. Croom Helm, Beckenham, Kent

Glaser BJ, Strauss AL 1967 The discovery of grounded theory: strategies for qualitative research. Aldine, Chicago

Glaser BJ, Strauss AL 1968 A time for dying. Aldine, Chicago

Hutchinson S 1986 Grounded theory the method. In: Munhall P, Oiler C (ed) Nursing research a qualitative approach. Appleton Century Crofts, New York, ch. 6

Kriedler M-H 1978 Meaning in suffering: a nursing dilemma. Unpublished doctoral dissertation, Teacher's College, Columbia University, New York

Kvale S 1983 The qualitative research interview. Journal of Phenomenology and Psychology 14 (2): 171-95

McLean GL 1992 Restoring the image: a grounded theory investigation of the meaning and experience of acute myeloid leukaemia. Unpublished thesis submitted for the degree of MPhil, University of Wales

Melia KM 1982 'Tell it as it is' – qualitative methodology and nursing research: understanding the student nurses' world. Journal of Advanced Nursing 7: 327-335

Merleau Ponty 1964 The primacy of perception. North Western University Press, Evanston

Munhall PL 1988 Ethical considerations in qualitative research. Western Journal of Nursing Research April 10 (2): 150-162

Nehemkis AM, Gerber KE, Charter RA 1984 The cancer ward. Patient perceptions – staff misperceptions. Psychotherapeutic Psycho-somatics 41: 42–47

Seligman ME 1975 Helplessness on depression, development and death. WH Freeman, San Francisco

Sontag S 1988 Illness as metaphor. Farrar, Straus & Giroux, New York

2. Ron

RON MILLER CAME FROM A STEEL-WORKING COMMUNITY. BORN AND RAISED in the Welsh valleys, he had lived near the works all his life. After he left school, he took up an apprenticeship as an electrician, and when he qualified, he went to work at the steelworks. He married Gwen when he was 20, and together they brought up their five children, three boys and two girls.

Although short in stature, Ron was a strong, rugged man. He was a man who had learned to look after himself. However, when he reached 47, his health began to fail. He was diagnosed as having rheumatoid arthritis. Initially he struggled to keep on working and supporting his family but, as the disease progressed, he was forced to seek early retirement. He gradually became increasingly disabled, unable to care for himself and totally dependent on others. In the late autumn of 1985, Ron's health deteriorated even further. Eventually, his doctor referred him to hospital, where he was diagnosed as having acute myeloid leukaemia. He was 52 years old.

Ron was admitted to Rhiannon Ward and was treated with cytotoxic chemotherapy. His disease responded quickly and he went into remission almost immediately. Unfortunately, he then contracted septicaemia and went into renal failure. He was transferred to the renal unit for haemodialysis and intensive therapy. Ron slowly recovered. He was discharged home for convalescence, and then began consolidation and maintenance chemotherapy in December 1985. A year later, in December 1986, a bone marrow transplant was performed. The success of the treatment was short-lived. 7 months later, in June 1987, Ron's disease relapsed. He was readmitted to Rhiannon for induction chemotherapy.

It was during this admission that I first met Ron. My earliest recollections of him are vague as our meetings were at night and were brief, perhaps a 5-minute conversation while I administered his intravenous therapy or a short chat after I had fulfilled his request for extra pillows and a strong cup of tea. The rest of the night he slept, buried under a pile of bedclothes as he attempted, albeit unsuccessfully, to exclude the night-time ward noises.

2. RON

During the daytime, Gwen was Ron's constant and faithful companion. Throughout the long, timeless days of chemotherapy and sickness, she remained at his bedside, only leaving the ward to eat, buy a newspaper or to sleep. In her absence, the two daughters Jan and Liz 'managed things at home'. In addition, they visited the hospital each afternoon, bringing with them fresh laundry supplies and moral support. The three boys, Alec, Steve and Ian, lived and worked abroad. They 'came home when they could'.

Once his treatment was completed, Ron was discharged home and followed up on an outpatient basis. He returned to the ward a few weeks later for a further course of treatment.

In August 1987, I happened to meet Ron on the ward. Following the completion of his second course of chemotherapy, he was waiting for his blood results to come through on the ward computer so that he could go home. With nothing to occupy his time, he was eager to chat. Towards the end of our conversation, he agreed to 'do an interview' with me. We arranged to meet the following week after his next doctor's appointment. As we parted, Ron warned me: 'It won't take long; I'm nowt mooch of a talker.'

---

19 August 1987

It was a cool, grey morning. When I arrived on the ward, I went in search of Ron. I soon found him. He was sitting quietly in the day room, dressed comfortably and smartly in a pair of cream trousers, a freshly laundered cotton shirt and a rich, dark-brown leather jacket. He was staring out of the window at the heavy, overcast sky. His 'bloods' had been taken, and he was waiting for the results. He nodded a greeting, and then together we made our way across the ward to the sister's office.

The sister's office was a model of busy confusion: the cupboards were filled to overflowing with a jumble of books and medical equipment, a filing cabinet was stuffed with an assortment of magazines and journal articles, the desk was cluttered with order forms, old records and reports, and the window-sill was covered with haphazard piles of old copies of the *Reader's Digest*, tattered paperbacks and textbooks bearing titles like *Essential Haematology*, *Cancer Nursing*, *Nursing Models* and *Nursing Theory*.

Ron and I made ourselves comfortable in two low easy chairs. I positioned a small stool between us and set up the tape-recorder. Ron grinned, folded his arms, leaned back in his chair and gazed around the room. A few moments later, he began to fidget. He wriggled in his chair, crossed and uncrossed his legs, folded and unfolded his arms and then started rubbing his hands together. Unfortunately, the chairs were covered with cream-coloured vinyl and every time Ron moved, his jacket cracked and squeaked as the leather rubbed against the vinyl.

A little surprised by Ron's evident anxiety, I tried to put him at ease by talking about something familiar to him. I asked him to tell me about his diagnosis.

'I was ill for 'bout a fortnight. The GPs didn't know what was wrong with me. I seen five GPs, and they didn't 'ave a clue!' Ron chuckled in disbelief. 'Anyway they sent me to Darrow where I 'ad a blood test, and that showed there was too many white cells in m' blood. Then a doctor come up from Benmore and give me a marrow.... I knew then that I was cooked. Well, 'e just told me that I was practically dyin'.... After that I started bleedin'. There was blood everywhere, back, front, everywhere. So they rushed me down 'ere, and after that I can't remember a lot, 'cos they shoved so much stuff into me, I didn't know whether I was comin' or goin'.... I'd no idea where I was. I 'ad 'allucinations, everythin' for 'bout 3 weeks.'

'You had hallucinations?' I interjected.

Ron nodded. 'Aye! I saw men in boxes, pictures on fire, telly on fire. They 'ad to put the telly under the bed.... It was terrible. I'd wake up and wonder where I was. I was frightened to go to sleep. There was these big gollywog efforts in little boxes. I told the wife not to touch the boxes, 'cos they was in there.' Ron grunted. 'And there were stars about the room.... A friend of mine come in, and I said, "Did you see the star up there?" 'E said, "No!" I'd point. "It's there!" 'Is wife says, "Go-on, the star. Aye! I see the star!"' Ron grunted again. 'But there weren't no star in the room. They were outside.... And I was terrible at night, Keith [a male night nurse] 'll tell you.... I pulled all them whatsanames off m' arms.'

'The infusion tubing?' I suggested

Ron turned to me and nodded again. 'Aye! I pulled 'em all off. I wanted to go 'ome, see. So I was gettin' out of bed the whole time, and they'd keep pullin' me back.' Ron laughed. 'I was off 'ome. Oh, I was bad!'

Apparently, Ron's confusion was a result of the severe septicaemia that developed after his first course of chemotherapy. Acutely ill, Ron's condition deteriorated rapidly. His kidneys failed and he was transferred to the renal unit for haemodialysis and intensive therapy. As Ron was not expected to survive, the whole family were contacted and summoned to the hospital. Steve and Ian were flown home from Africa and Germany, respectively.

It was December 1985. Aware of his circumstances, but too ill to care, Ron slowly began to recover. That Christmas was a time of celebration. After only a single course of chemotherapy, Ron's disease had gone into remission. Moreover, his arthritis had also vanished. Ron described the events leading up to his recovery.

'It went as soon as the chemo finished. There was nothin' there. It went completely. When I come in, I couldn't walk, couldn't bend m' knees...blinkin' bedpans. The nurses, they 'ad to bend m' knees for me.... But I did all right with that chemo. I don't know 'ow it done it, but it cured it, and I 'aven't 'ad no trouble since. It killed the lot!'

Due to Ron's excellent response to treatment, the doctors decided to perform a bone marrow rescue. The procedure was planned for December 1986. In the meantime, he was given consolidation chemotherapy and then maintenance chemotherapy.

'How were you during that period?' I asked.

'Oh, champion!' Ron declared. 'Back to 13 stone, I was 9.... It was them steroids [Ron's renal failure was treated with steroid therapy]. That's 'ow I got so big.'

I nodded. 'They make you very hungry, don't they?'

'Cor! 'Ungry – if it walked, I 'ad to eat it. I was starvin'!' Ron laughed. 'But I was only comin' up 'ere for blood tests. Then I 'ad me op' for this Port-A-Cath.' He smiled and patted his chest happily. 'No, I'm wrong. First op' they took out the marrow, and that were no problem. It weren't even sore. I was a little bit rougher when they put the Port-A-Cath in 'cos they 'ad trouble with m' neck.'

Although many of the symptoms characteristic of rheumatoid arthritis resolved following Ron's initial course of chemotherapy, his neck remained stiff and inflexible. Ron's Port-A-Cath was inserted under a general anaesthetic. Prior to his operation, the anaesthetist experienced great difficulty in performing the intubation. Ron was surprised. He assumed that any stiffness would 'disappear during the anaesthetic'.

A bone marrow rescue was performed the following Christmas, in December 1986. After the procedure, Ron went home to convalesce. His recovery was rapid and uneventful. Within a few weeks, his marrow was functioning normally and he was able to resume his normal daily activities. For example, several evenings during the week he went down to 'the club' for a chat and a game of pool. Greatly encouraged by his rapid return to health and freedom, Ron enjoyed comparing himself with the other transplant patients, many of whom were still dependent on supportive transfusion therapy several months post-transplant.

In June 1987, Ron and Gwen went on holiday to Greece. A fortnight after their return, Ron attended the outpatient clinic. A routine bone marrow biopsy was performed; the bone marrow sample was packed with leukaemic cells. The leukaemia had relapsed.

Ron was not surprised by the result. 'Well, I'd started to go off m' food about a week before I come in 'ere, so I thought somethin' might be wrong. 'Cos, once you start to go off your food, there's somethin' wrong. That's what I found with this anyway. Now I've started buildin' up with the eatin' again, so I 'ope that's a sign that the chemo's killed it off.' Ron shifted his position in his chair. His leather jacket cracked and squeaked. 'It's m' birthday next month and then the wife's, and then there's Christmas. I've got to last till then 'cos all the boys are comin' 'ome. I 'aven't seen Steve, the one in Africa, for 2 years now, not since I was due to die, like.' He nodded. 'Ah! I were lucky to pull through that time. It were rough.' Ron paused, then looked up at me and grinned. 'But I don't look beyond Christmas, 'cos I'll be in. No, there's no future for me. I know what's goin' to 'appen sooner or later. I only 'ope it's delayed, mind.'

Ron fell silent and then continued, 'Ah! But it's 'ard work back and forth 'ere. I'm tired and I get fed up. But if I do come on all right, it'll be OK. That once a month at the clinic is livin'. I don't mind that goin'

2. RON

to the clinic and goin' back with an all-clear. It's great!' He laughed as he remembered his clinic experience. 'I used to worry a day or two before, mind. I knew in m'self that I was all right, but I was all of a bobble, thinkin', "What are they going to do with me?" It's them marrows, I 'ate 'em!'

'You hate them? Why is that?' I asked.

'I don't know.... It isn't painful, but it's weird. They're just 'orrible!'

'Can you describe one?' I prompted.

'Well, it ain't a nice feelin' goin' in, 'cos you can feel it pushin' in, and pluck as it goes in the middle, like. Then when they drag it out, it comes from your toes. It's not very pleasant at all. It makes me sweat.... I don't mind tellin' you; I get nervous with anythin' about 'em. But I 'ope I'll 'ave a dozen more, a couple of dozen.' Ron smiled mischievously. 'You should try one. It don't 'urt, and the doctors'd do one no trouble. You wouldn't 'ave to ask nobody, then, 'cos you'd know exactly what it were like!' He chuckled as he considered the prospect of my undergoing a bone marrow aspiration. Then becoming more serious, he added, 'Ah! But it's an expensive 'obby comin' up 'ere every week. It's six quid a time....'

Ron talked about the financial difficulties associated with illness. When he was diagnosed as having rheumatoid arthritis, he became eligible for a disability pension and an attendance allowance. In addition, during the time he was hospitalised or while he was receiving treatment as an outpatient, he was able to apply for travelling expenses and general subsistence payments. Unfortunately, compared with his former wage of £200 a week, the benefits appeared to be a pittance. To illustrate his argument, he cited the example of the special welfare payment he recently received. The payment was supposed to cover the additional costs he and his family incurred over the Christmas week. The cheque amounted to £20 which, in his words, 'wasn't a terrible lot!'

Aware of his financial hardships, Ron's family and friends tried to help. The children contributed regularly to the family fund, while his friends at the club organised a one-off collection for him. They raised a total of £200 and gave it to Ron and Gwen as a contribution towards their increased travelling and living expenses.

Considering the financial losses that Ron incurred with illness, did he regret his inability to work?

Ron shook his head vigorously. 'Oh, I don't want to bother with that no more. No, I've finished with that.... If you've not got your 'ealth, you've 'ad it on that job, 'specially on that job!'

Surprised by his aggressive response, I wondered if Ron believed his job in the steelworks had contributed to his illness? He repudiated my assumption vehemently.

'No! I'd suffered from rheumatoid arthritis for years, and it could possibly 've 'ad somethin' to do with that. I 'ad dozens of X-rays. Then again, it could 've been all the pills. I took thousands of them Distalgesics...and I took Opren for months and that didn't do people a lot of good, did it?'

'It sounds as though you try and find reasons for the disease's development?' I suggested.

'Aye! I do think about it, but I 'aven't got a clue really.' Ron spoke slowly and thoughtfully. 'There's the chemical works up by us.... They burn anythin' there, and all the smoke and stuff drifts up our way. I don't know if it's a black spot, but old Greg [a friend and fellow leukaemic patient who died in May 1987] used to deliver stuff there.' He grunted. 'But I shouldn't imagine it was that. No, I think it's just somethin' that pops up, just comes on you. It don't run in families or anythin'.' We sat in silence for several minutes. Ron stared gloomily out of the window at the grey, deserted courtyard below. He turned back towards me, a sad expression on his face. 'When you get over the 50 mark, somethin's always goin' to 'appen to you. It could be an 'eart attack, angina, stomach problems; you've always got to expect somethin'.... With most of 'em, you can live normally – you ain't goin' to die tomorrow; but with leukaemia, it's day to day. The treatment's awful, and you never feel well. No, I wouldn't wish it on a dog.... It's these youngsters in their twenties I feel sorry for. They've got plenty of guts, mind, but I don't know 'ow they manage.' He looked up at me. 'They 'aven't got a future, 'ave they?'

Instead of encouraging Ron to expand his thoughts, I questioned him about suffering. 'Do you feel that you have suffered?'

Ron nodded vigorously and said, 'Aye! Oh, aye!'

'In what way?'

'Well, a lot mentally. There's not a lot of physical pain, but mentally...'

'Can you put it into words?' I asked.

He hesitated before replying, 'Well, I'm thinkin' of dyin' all the time. It's always on m' mind, and I know it's only a matter of time.... But I do 'ope for the best. The doctors promised me 3–10 years so I took their word for it. Then it went *pop!*' He laughed. 'But I knew it would come back, 'cos it's only a matter of time.'

'You expected more time?'

Ron nodded. 'I did! I did! I expected at least the 12 months. Others 've 'ad that and more, like Jeremy and Mary, so I thought "I deserve more'n that." But I knew it would come back....' He smiled wistfully. 'And you lose your 'air. Four times I've lost me 'air, which isn't very nice when you've got a big nose like me, 'cos it shows up!'

'Do the physical side-effects concern you?' I asked.

'No, I don't bother much. Though I did find it cold when I lost me 'air. I used to go to bed with a bobble cap on. It's cold, and you miss it!' He paused and grinned. 'I'd go to Rhiannon and there'd be six bald 'eads. I was all right there.'

I smiled. 'You felt at home?'

'Ah!' He agreed. 'I felt at 'ome. Six of us bald. It ain't so bad when you're all in, but it's a bit depressin' when they go on like....' His voice trailed off to a whisper and he began to cough. 'I'm afraid to ask now. Well, all m' pals 've gone.'

'Did you ask in the beginning?'

'No!' Ron waved his arm in the direction of the ward. 'They kept on tellin' me. I didn't want to bloody know! It's a shock to the system every time, 'specially with Greg....'

'How did you find out about him?' I wondered aloud.

'The social worker told the wife, like. She thought we'd want to know. When we 'eard, we went over and stopped the weekend at 'is place.... All the others've gone now as well, 'bout a dozen of 'em....'

During his illness, Ron had kept himself apart from many of the other patients. He had few patient friends. I asked him to describe these friendships.

'There was only Greg and Chris, oh, and Jeremy.' His face wrinkled into an allusive grin. "E makes me smile, 'e does. You know, 'e 'ad two shirts on one day, a pullover and a woolly 'at. 'E's a card!' Ron chuckled to himself, enjoying the memory. 'Whenever 'e were in, 'e'd get 'is knittin' out. 'E'd sit on 'is bed and knit, and 'e'd talk. 'Is wife's the same, mind. They're good talkers, fair play.' He began to chuckle again. Then stopping abruptly, he said, 'I don't think there's a cure, is there? They may find one eventually, but...'

Unable to give an answer, I asked, 'Did you expect the transplant to cure you?

He nodded. 'Well, they say there's 80% chance of cure, but I knew it would come back. It's only a matter of time. Ah! It'll nail me in the end.' He shrugged his shoulders as if to convey his indifference. 'But you get so ill, you don't worry.'

'You don't worry?' I repeated his words.

'Well, when you're 'ealthy, it do worry you. But with this chemo, you don't know 'ow ill you are. Just 'cos you aren't peein', that don't worry you. The nurses are scared stiff 'cos they knows more than you, but you're just laid in bed, and you 'aven't got much idea what's 'appenin', like....' Ron fell silent.

'How did you feel when the leukaemia came back?' I asked.

'Oh, disappointed. I do get depressed and down in the mouth.... I want to grizzle all the time. I can't 'elp it. I must be in a state of depression....' He nodded as if to confirm his own diagnosis. 'Ah! The tears come easy now. They never did before.'

'The tears come easy?' I echoed Ron's words.

He gave another affirmative nod. 'Ah!'

'You've got a bit softer?' I suggested.

'Ah! Softer, that's it. I've got softer.' He began to laugh. 'I cried a bit, mind, the first time I 'ad it.... I wasn't surprised I 'ad it, but I think it got me down.'

'It got you down?'

'Yep. It got me down.'

'What helps you come out it, out of the depression?' I asked.

'Oh, I don't think I come out of it. See, anythin' can upset me.' He paused and smiled. 'It's nothin' serious, like toppin' m'self or anythin'....'

'Did you consider that?' I ventured.

'Well, I thought about it in the beginnin'.' He pointed to the small, high, narrow windows in the office and laughed. 'I tried them windows, but I didn't like the drop!' He hesitated before he attempted to explain the thoughts that had driven him to contemplating suicide. 'It's the thought of cancer, the painful death. That's all I could think of: "It's goin' to be painful...."'

'Do you think about death itself?' I asked.

'No, I don't do nothin' like that. I think it's all a big sleep, that's all.'

'A big sleep?' I reflected.

'Yep! 'Fraid so! The end's the end, so I've got it all laid out.' Ron spoke quietly and slowly, pausing between each sentence. 'I won't leave much money...just enough. And it's all marked out at the church. I'll be near the club, 'bout a mile from 'ome.... Gwen can visit me then, and she can call in after at the club and 'ave a chat with 'er friends.... No, you've all got to die sometime. I was just 'opin' I'd die of old age....' He smiled at the irony of his situation. 'But I've got to keep at it, 'aven't I? Survive as long as I can.... I'll go all the way.' He paused and reflected, 'I don't know whether I'll go 'ome near the end or just stay 'ere. I've been thinkin' about it, but...'

'Have you talked to Gwen about it?'

'Yeah! I 'ave.' He spoke quietly, a look of resignation on his face. 'Play it by ear, that's the best way. Well, best be goin', then! They've likely got the news by now....'

Our conversation ended abruptly as Ron returned to the ward to find out his blood results. I departed shortly after him, my mind full of jumbled thoughts and impressions from our time together. I felt a deep sadness for Ron. In conversation the previous week, he had expressed feelings of anger and bitterness regarding his relapse. Now these feelings had been replaced by a sense of hopelessness and futility. Part of his depression could be attributed to the side-effects of chemotherapy. Nevertheless, his depression was profound and he appeared to be preoccupied with thoughts of pain and death.

* * *

Ron responded well to the induction chemotherapy and, by the end of August 1987, his disease had once again gone into remission. Consolidation chemotherapy was given and he was discharged home. Once a month, he returned to the outpatient clinic for a follow-up appointment. Despite lingering complaints of fatigue, anorexia and shortness of breath, Ron's health gradually improved and he was able to live a more normal life.

After the first interview, I was concerned that Ron had found the conversation difficult and distressing. A few months later, he dispelled my fears. During a chance meeting in clinic, he asked if I wanted to do a second interview. Similarly, he allayed my concerns regarding the structure of our talk. Convinced that I had asked too many questions and had prevented him from sharing his thoughts and feelings, I was surprised when he asked me to maintain my approach to the interview. He said that he preferred to be asked specific questions, and explained, 'I just forget things, otherwise.' We arranged to meet before his next clinic appointment in November.

11 November 1987

It was raining heavily as I cycled to the hospital. Despite being late morning, the clinic was still packed with people when I arrived. The corridor and main waiting area were both full. Patients and their relatives sat chatting to one another. Names were shouted as patients were summoned to have their blood drawn, their urine tested or their blood pressure and weight measured. The clinic buzzed with the sounds of conversation, banging cupboard doors and clinking bottles. Ron and I retreated into the relative peace of a vacant examination room.

The examination room was starkly furnished. It contained only a sink, an examination couch and a large, wooden desk. On the desk lay a large, well-used, green blotting pad, a telephone and a new prescription pad. We pulled two chairs up to the desk and sat down.

Ron looked well. His hair had grown since our last meeting, and he was neatly dressed in a bright yellow sweater, a white cotton shirt and a pair of fawn trousers. While I set up the tape-recorder, Ron brought me up to date with the details of his illness. He spoke quietly. His voice sounded flat and dispirited. He was tired.

The following Monday, Ron was to be admitted to Rhiannon for a 3-day course of maintenance chemotherapy. He was ambivalent about the prospect of treatment. Realising that it would reduce the likelihood of a rapid relapse, he welcomed the therapy. However, at the same time, his fear of sickness caused him to dread the treatment. Despite his fears, he was determined to follow the doctors' advice, as he felt that they were 'in control' and that 'they knew best'. Although dependence upon the medical staff gave Ron a feeling of security, he realised that his future remained uncertain. He could live for years; on the other hand he might die in 2 weeks' time. Moreover, his admission to hospital only served to remind him of his situation. The ward represented many sad memories for Ron. It was a place where many of his friends had died. Ron was unable to escape from his thoughts of death.

'I'm thinkin' about it all the time.'

'You're thinking about the leukaemia, or possibly dying?'

He nodded, looking down at the floor. 'The leukaemia, possibly dyin'. It's on m' mind the whole time. I 'ave moments, but I can't really be 'appy 'cos I know I'm not goin' to recover, so I've just got to take it.... There's other people worse off than me, mind, people in pain. I ain't in pain, not yet, anyway....'

'Is there still that doubt in your mind?' I wondered aloud.

'Aye! I do think you 'ave a lot of pain when you go.... Some go easy; others go 'ard. You've just got to take a chance with it.' He grunted. 'As long as I go nice and quiet, I don't mind....'

Ron went on to explain how he had seen a couple of people die following a brain haemorrhage. Having explored the various types of death that people with leukaemia were likely to have, he confessed that he wanted to die of pneumonia and just 'run out of breath'.

Despite his apparent flippancy regarding death, Ron was deeply distressed when a colleague died. In this situation, death symbolised the loss of a friend and a fellow sufferer. He spoke slowly and thoughtfully.

'It upsets me, like. I try to forget it, but I don't forget it really. It's on m' mind the whole time. No, there's no cure, is there? So I go from day to day and just 'ope for the best.' He turned away from me and looked morosely at the examination couch. 'I can't escape from m' thoughts, they're all inside....' He looked back at me, patted his head and grinned. 'Unless I cut me 'ead off, then they do vanish!'

The only thing that enabled Ron to escape from reality was humour. When he was in with his 'buddies' on the ward or the outpatient clinic, they would 'get together and have a bit of fun.' 'All in the same boat', they would pass the time, telling funny stories and jokes in an effort to raise one another's spirits. Gallows humour was common among them. Sadly, as soon as Ron returned home and was alone, the fears and concerns came flooding back. Each day was the same. The fears were always there. He couldn't even lose them by keeping himself busy. He was always tired, and so his quiet daily routine of watching television, feeding the chickens, walking the dog and sleeping failed to dispel the underlying tension that had become a natural and accepted part of his existence.

Four evenings a week, Gwen worked at the club. Occasionally, Ron drove her to and from work. When he went to collect her, he would stop and have a drink at the bar before they went home. However, even these visits to the club didn't alleviate his anxiety.

'I pick 'er up at 10 o'clock and 'ave a pint or two.... I got m' own glass there, case somebody don't like it and thinks it's catchin' or somethin'.... But it ain't so bad. It's livin'. But the days do go quick!' In general, all his days passed quickly. 'It was the same in 'ospital.... Well,' he chuckled, 'I'm in bed 'alf the time!'

Ron was familiar with the isolation that resulted from having a life-threatening illness. He explained how people were often unable to comprehend his disease and consequently responded to him according to his current physical appearance. Ron was deeply hurt by their lack of understanding and insensitivity.

'They 'aven't got a clue what it's like. They don't understand. I think to m'self, "You ought to try a little bit of it. You ought to see what it's like for a few days...."' He grinned at the thought. 'Oh, they know all about cancer! It's painful! But with leukaemia, they see you walkin' around, and there's nothin' wrong with you.' He gestured towards the waiting room, full of patients and their families. 'Some of 'em in 'ere look normal: their 'air's back; they've put a bit of weight on, and they look champion! People don't know that they're dyin' and that the doctors can't do no more for 'em. No, they don't know what I've been through....'

'They don't know what you've been through?' I repeated.

'No. They 'aven't got a clue!'

'Has it changed you?' I asked.

'Aye! I'm tolerant now. I don't get uptight....' He grinned again. 'I used to get me 'air off, but I don't bother now.'

I laughed as I began to imagine Ron getting his hair off. A picture formed in my mind. I questioned him further. 'What does that entail?'

'Well, they're insensitive. Like m' brother-in-law and a couple of others, they just don't understand.... They've seen me when I was ill, and they say, "You've aged 40 years, like!" Ron snorted. 'Then they'd say, "How the 'ell did you come out of it?"'

'What did you say to them?' I wondered aloud.

'I told 'em I'd no idea!' He smiled to himself as he recounted the situation. 'But the spark's gone now. If I'd been 'ealthy, I'd 've got 'em down with one 'ook. No, the old spark's gone. I'm very mild. Things don't bother me now, unless m' daughters are out late till 1 o'clock, then I do worry, and I get mad.' He looked up at me and continued, 'I worry about the family, but they're all grown up now' He grinned again. 'They worry about us instead....'

Ron described how the children had gradually taken over many of the family responsibilities. Recently, for instance, they had bought him and Gwen a new car. He enjoyed going out for an afternoon drive in the country; he enjoyed the independence and freedom that travelling allowed him. Unfortunately, his driving skills had deteriorated due to the neurological impairment caused by his chemotherapy, and he therefore shared the driving with Gwen.

Shared driving was only one facet of Gwen's commitment to Ron. During his illness, she shared everything with him. They did everything together. Gwen was always there at his side. According to Ron, she'd 'gone all the way'.

'What about the rest of the family?' I asked.

'Oh, [the leukaemia] don't affect them. They don't seem to know 'ow serious it is. As long as I'm around, that's all they want. No, Gwen's the only one that's really 'elped. She does everythin' for me. I don't even 'ave to get m'self a cup of tea. She gets it for me.... I do get m' own breakfast sometimes. Well, it's just bread 'n' butter and a piece of fruit. It's funny, I never used to like fruit.' He paused reflectively. 'I'd 'ave eggs 'n' bacon when I were workin', but I've changed over now.... But Gwen gets it for me most of the time. She does everythin' for me.'

'Do you find that hard, being so dependent on Gwen?'

'No, I'm used to it now....' Ron refuted.

Voices sounded outside in the corridor and the door opened. A little embarrassed, the clinic nurse apologised for disturbing us and quickly closed the door. Ron glanced at his watch. Worried that we were interfering with the busy clinic schedule and Ron's appointment, I started to bring the interview to a close.

'Have you learnt anything from your illness?'

Ron leant back in his chair, folded his arms and pondered his reply. 'Well, I'm braver than what I thought. It's bloody 'ard work keepin' alive, and I've seen a few give up.' He chuckled. 'I'll never give up! Not till I'm too ill, but I won't worry about that. No, I'm lookin' forward to Christmas and then an 'oliday. I'm not lookin' too far ahead, mind...just a couple of months, that's all.... But I'll need some sleep 'afore then, 'cos this next 3 days'll knock me about a bit.' He stroked his head. 'And I'll be bald again, for the fifth time.'

'Do you mind? Being bald, I mean.'

Ron laughed. 'No, I don't worry, but I'm old, see.'

I challenged him, 'Do you really feel that you are old?'

Ron pretended to look surprised and said, '54 is old, isn' it?' Then becoming serious, he added, 'It does seem old, 'specially in the mornin's.... No, I've been lucky so far. I've 'ad the 2 years, but I can't go on. It'll catch me one day'

The telephone rang, intruding into our conversation. Ron leaned forward, glanced at his watch and announced, '1.30! I'd best be goin'.... I'll see 'ow this marrow is, then. I get the results Monday when I go in, so I 'ope it's a good 'un.' He grunted. 'If it ain't, they'll just 'ave to give me some stronger stuff, that's all.... But I feel in m'self that I'm OK, so I think the marrow's all right.'

Our conversation ended as Ron stood up and went out into the clinic. Once again, I was left with the impression that he was struggling with feelings of doubt, fear and depression. Although more at peace with himself, he appeared despondent and there was a sense of hopelessness and resignation about his attitude towards his leukaemia. Moreover, as we talked, he emphasised the fact that his 'old spark' had gone and that he was more placid now. I was left wondering what the old Ron had been like, before his personality had been transformed by illness and his struggle with uncertainty.

* * * * *

3. *Dorothy*

BORN IN 1926, DOROTHY WILLIAMS GREW UP DURING THE YEARS OF THE Depression. Although money and food were scarce, her home life was happy and secure. Her parents believed that 'a good life was a happy life' and she was therefore brought up in an atmosphere of strict discipline combined with love. Shortly before the start of the Second World War, Dorothy began to attend a local state school. A little above average in class, she did well in her studies and she enjoyed her schooling. Indeed, she remembered her sadness at leaving school and starting work. After a couple of temporary office jobs, Dorothy joined the Civil Service as a Clerical Assistant. 2 years later she met an architect called Tom. In 1947, they were married and Dorothy left the Civil Service (in those days, married woman were not allowed to remain in the Service).

Dorothy's married life was happy and full. After the birth of her two sons, Kenneth and Michael, she immersed herself in family life. She devoted her time and energies into caring for Tom and 'her boys'. When the boys left home to go to college and later to marry, Dorothy and Tom 'missed them terribly'. However, the family ties remained strong, and the Williams's home was always open to 'the boys', their wives and their children.

In May 1987, Dorothy was diagnosed as having acute myeloid leukaemia. She responded well to treatment and her disease went into remission after her first course of induction chemotherapy. Normally, Dorothy would not be considered a suitable candidate for bone marrow transplantation. At 61 years of age, she was too old to fulfil the strict admission criteria for transplantation. However, due to her remarkable attitude and her excellent response to treatment, the medical staff decided to give her a bone marrow rescue.

Dorothy was an exceptionally warm and outgoing woman. She loved people and she enjoyed nothing more than spending time with her family and friends. A wonderful conversationalist, she soon became popular with the staff and patients following her admission to the ward.

3. DOROTHY

I remember my first meeting with Dorothy clearly. It was a cool June night, and I was on duty. Dorothy was a patient on Rhiannon. She had been admitted for a course of consolidation chemotherapy. At 2.30 am she rang her call bell and requested an antiemetic injection. After administering the drug, I stayed with her. We were not busy on the ward and it was obvious that Dorothy needed to talk.

In the conversation that ensued, Dorothy described an encounter that she had had with a member of staff earlier that evening. Apparently, a few hours after receiving her chemotherapy, she started to feel nauseous. She rang her bell and asked for treatment. A few minutes later, a young houseman came with the prescribed drug and nervously asked her to show him where in the Hickman line he should inject the drug. Lying quietly in bed, Dorothy told me, 'I became frightened and told him that I wasn't feeling sick any more.... Well, I didn't want him making a mess of my line! There are lots of clips and things, and it's easy to undo the wrong bit. Anyway, he flung the syringe on one side and said that I could get one of the nursing staff to give the drug if I needed it.... I was so upset by his attitude, and now I can't get the incident out of my mind....'

Over the next hour, Dorothy shared with me some of her concerns regarding her illness, her treatment and her family. Opening a window into her world, she described some of the small, but important struggles that she faced each day. She explored her feelings of anxiety, fear, guilt, anger, resentment and depression.

Over the following months, our acquaintance grew. As Dorothy underwent chemotherapy, we met periodically on the ward and in the outpatient clinic. At these meetings, Dorothy would briefly bring me up to date with her illness and would then chat happily about her family. I followed her progress with interest. Dorothy coped well with her illness: she gradually learnt about her disease and acquired the many skills of a leukaemic patient. In August, I arranged to visit Dorothy in her home.

24 August 1987

Dorothy and Tom lived only a short distance from my own home. It was a warm, sunny afternoon and it took me only 10 minutes to walk round to their house. The Williamses lived in a large, red-brick house. The property was surrounded on all sides: a low stone wall extended around the front garden, while a high wooden fence sheltered the large and private back garden.

I opened the gate and walked up the path to the front door. I rang the door-bell and a dog began to bark noisily. A few moments later, Tom opened the door. He welcomed me graciously and showed me into the lounge.

Dorothy was sitting on the sofa. She wore an attractive, loose-fitting summer dress. The dress had a delicate flowery print that matched her pale pink turban perfectly. Her broad, round face was tanned and hairless from the chemotherapy. She wore no make-up. A careful arrangement of freshly cut flowers from the garden stood in a vase on the television cabinet and a set of heavy, floral curtains framed the large picture-windows that opened on to the garden at the rear of the house. At the far end of the lounge, two smaller windows looked out on to the road. Paintings and family photographs hung on the walls, a delightful mix of family groupings, wedding pictures and old school portraits. Speaking slowly and thoughtfully, Dorothy described her experiences over the last few months. Her eyes glowed with reminiscence as she recounted the trauma of her diagnosis. Her soft Welsh accent made her words sound rich and warm.

'I thought I had a winter cold, like everybody else. My eyes were bad. They were runny and sore...and really, it was because I couldn't use make-up that I thought I'd better go to the doctor. The doctor thought I had a virus, so she sent me for a blood test, and 9 o'clock the next morning, she was up here, hammering on the door. She said that they'd found something wrong at the hospital and would I go back to the clinic that day. I did, and they took more blood tests. Then I had to go again the next morning, and they said they were going to do a bone marrow test. When they said that, I felt that it was much worse than I had anticipated.... Then they told me; it was May 1st.' Dorothy paused for a few moments and then continued, 'I was fortunate. I went into hospital straight-away. I saw Sister Jones and Dr Roberts on Rhiannon Ward, and they were fantastic! They got us over the initial shock and told us that there was treatment available, and so I started the treatment....'

'What did you feel like when you were told about the leukaemia and the treatment?' I asked

'I think before you're ill, you're a bit like an ostrich....' Dorothy began.

'You put your head in the sand, and it doesn't affect you. I was completely shattered, completely shattered. Well, before I was ill, I never went to the doctor's, and I wasn't interested in drugs or medicine at all, so I didn't even know that there was a cure for leukaemia. We thought it was a death sentence, so we were very pleased that there was treatment available. We were warned that it wasn't very pleasant, but that's all we had. We had to jump on the bandwagon and make the most of it, because there was no alternative.' Dorothy glanced at me quickly and exclaimed, 'But right from the beginning when they said I had leukaemia, I've had a terrific strength, and I knew that we just had to get on with it, look it in the face and get on with it.'

Dorothy fell silent. Out in the hall, a clock chimed. It sounded three ringing chimes – 3 o'clock. As the chimes faded, Dorothy said hurriedly, 'There's no point in looking for other treatments because there aren't any. I don't know what would happen if you didn't get into remission? That's your lot, I suppose. And I don't know if they can keep people in remission for a long time, just keep them going with platelets and things. So I have to put up with it, don't I?' Dorothy's face wore an expression of resignation.

I shook my head in response and asked, 'What helped you put up with the treatment?'

'Well, I mentioned before that Rhiannon is an exceptional ward. It's mainly because of the sister's attitude, and her attitude goes right the way down through the staff.... She's always busy. I've never seen her not doing anything, and I just think she's a remarkable woman. Although I've never spoken to her in depth, because...' At this point, Dorothy lowered her voice to a whisper as though she was frightened that someone might overhear what she was about to say, '...because she's never got the time. But I think she must be a very religious woman. She's very caring; she's very soft, which is surprising because you'd think she'd have to be a bit on the hard side to deal with people like me.'

'Why's that?' I enquired.

Dorothy hesitated and then replied, 'Well, people die there, and some people aren't very nice to deal with either. And she's very soft; she's very emotional, and she cries easily. So I think that she'd find it very difficult on the ward, very difficult....'

'You sound concerned.' I commented.

'Yes,' Dorothy affirmed, 'because I admire her.' She glanced at me quickly. 'You know she's leaving?' I nodded my response and Dorothy went on, 'Although I'm sorry for the ward and myself, I think it will do her good to have a change. But I do think her attitude and Dr Roberts's really put Tom and me on the right footing to face up to things. We felt that they were 100% behind us, and, without them, I don't think we'd have coped with things half as well as we have. Tom feels exactly the same as me. It's not only Sister Jones, there's all the staff that report to her, the staff nurses, all the nurses, everyone from the girls who serve the meals when you don't want to eat to the cleaners who come in to do your room, they're all marvellous. I've never yet come across anybody who didn't do the right thing or say the right thing. Whoever decided on how to run Rhiannon Ward, did it just right. I only hope it continues the same. But it's all changing; everything is changing....'

During her illness, Dorothy developed close friendships with four other leukaemic patients on the ward. Diagnosed within a few months of each other, they formed a tightly-knit group. Theirs was a unique intimacy that grew as a result of shared experiences and feelings. With emotion in her voice, Dorothy described the group dynamic.

'I found that I became very involved with the other patients: Dave, Rachel, Emily and Ralph. We were all on the same sort of level, and when we were all in together, we used to meet in the day room for a chat. As far as I'm concerned, I've had terrific help from Dave.' Dorothy paused and smiled.

'Can you describe how he helped you?' I encouraged.

'Well, Dave was diagnosed 3 months before I was, so he'd had more treatment than me. He'd done things that I'd never done, and he used to explain them to me. He'd tell me that it was nothing to worry about, a bit uncomfortable perhaps, but nothing too bad. We talked to each other and we had a great many laughs with each other. We gave each other good morale.... It helped just having someone who knew what I was talking about....' She paused and sighed. 'But we can adjust. We've had warnings, and this treatment is available so we must make the most of it.'

3. DOROTHY

Judging from her facial expression, her words and her tone of voice, I realised that Dorothy had probably heard about Dave's relapse. Dave had relapsed at the weekend immediately following his discharge from the transplant unit. On Sunday, I had met and spoken with Dave and his wife Paula. Aware of Dorothy's sensitive nature, the couple had hoped to prevent her from hearing the news before she was admitted for her own transplant. I wondered how the news had affected Dorothy.

'You've heard about Dave's relapse then?' I murmured.

Dorothy nodded. After a brief hesitation, she began to speak. Her voice sounded flat and dispirited, betraying the emotion she evidently felt. 'Yes, it was a shock. It was a disappointment, really. Dave's been very ill. Apparently, he was very ill when he was diagnosed, and I've seen him very ill, but I was surprised that Emily's didn't do, because she never seemed as bad as Dave.' (A week after Dave's recurrence was realised, Emily also relapsed. She too had undergone treatment for a bone marrow rescue.) 'But it was a blow, especially with both of them together.... But we did know that the treatment isn't 100% successful because, in all fairness, the doctors did talk to us about it. Last week we talked to Dr Green about the success rate and everything. So if it's not a success, I start all over again. It's as simple as that. And there again, I'm very lucky. Because we live near the hospital, I can spend a lot of time at home....'

Having altered the direction of the conversation, Dorothy began to relax. I followed her lead and didn't pursue her thoughts and feelings about Dave. Recognising her pain, I allowed her to continue describing her current treatment and her new double life. Nowadays, Dorothy's time was divided into time at home and time in hospital. Accustomed to the therapeutic regime associated with her leukaemia, she enjoyed an increasing amount of freedom and control over her illness. Her treatment, particularly the milder consolidation therapy, was often given on an outpatient basis. Dorothy attended the ward for blood tests, the administration of a cytotoxic injection and/or the fitting of a syringe pump*. Once her daily treatment had been given, she returned home. If a problem developed while she was at home, she returned to the ward. Thankfully, if a crisis occurred and

---

* The syringe pump facilitated the slow administration of cytosine and could be worn at home. Once the syringe was empty, Dorothy returned to the ward. Here the needle was removed from her arm and the pump was disconnected.

she was alone, Dorothy was only minutes away from the ward and the safety of 'expert' care givers. She told me about one such crisis.

'One afternoon, I was sitting in the garden. About tea-time, I felt a bit hot, so I thought I'd go up and have a wash and change my dress. When I took my dress off, I saw that it was bleeding where my pump had gone in. I phoned the ward, and they said, "You have to come in." So, as Tom wasn't home, I took a taxi, and in 15 minutes, I was back on the ward and everything was seen to.'

Now, in remission, Dorothy felt fit and healthy. She had resumed her normal life and her days were filled with activity: performing household chores, entertaining family and a few close friends, reading and doing crossword puzzles. Earlier in her treatment, when her blood counts were low and her humoral resistance was impaired, she and Tom had decided to implement a 'no visitors' policy. Only direct family members and close friends were exempt from the restrictions as they were aware of the need to stay away if they had an infection. Later, even though her 'counts' returned to normal, Dorothy had continued to restrict visitors to her home. Now her goal was to be fit for Christmas, and she had no intention of jeopardising her goal by contracting an infection.

'This year, we're going to have a real family Christmas with all the grandchildren. I'm afraid to go out in case I get an infection, and so I don't really mind staying in. That's why I'm glad that I don't have to stay in hospital for my treatment. I always pick something up while I'm in, and I should hate to be on Rhiannon for Christmas.' Dorothy turned and gazed out of the window. 'But they can't really tell if it's a success immediately. They have to wait quite a long time. 6 months, isn't it?' She looked back at me, a puzzled expression on her face. She accepted my nod of affirmation and continued, 'But if everything goes well, we'll have a nice Christmas, and if not...' – she grunted – '...if not, we'll start all over again. But if everything works out, I'm hoping that we can go on holiday in June or towards the end of the summer, go abroad to Florida and then on a cruise. And if it doesn't, we just have to hope on getting to remission quite a few times....'

'Have you thought about that possibility?' I suggested.

'Well, I do think about it, especially since last weekend. I know we'd be terribly disappointed for a while, but if it does happen, we'll just have to drag ourselves together and reorganise. I'm sure it must be terrible for a few days, because you pin everything on first of all getting to remission and then to transplant. I've been lucky so far and, as I say, I do get this terrific strength, so I'm not afraid.'

Intrigued by this concept, I tried to draw her out a little in conversation. 'An inner strength?'

Dorothy nodded. 'Yes! Yes! I rarely go to church, but I think I'm very religious.'

'In what way?' I rejoined.

After a long pause, Dorothy began to tell me about her belief in God. Brought up within the Church of England, she clung to the principles outlined in the Bible. She believed that Christ and his disciples were 'good men' and that Christ's teachings were essential to an ordered and peaceful world. However, she was unable to accept the truth of his divinity and she was confused by his crucifixion. She therefore felt a hypocrite when she attended church. While Dorothy was on the ward, however, she was visited by her local vicar and the hospital chaplain. These visits proved to be 'a great comfort' to her.

'When I'm better, I will go to church again. I must try, because I've had this terrific inner strength. I feel that all the prayers said by friends and people in the church are like a protection. I don't know how to describe it...I don't think it's a man with long white hair who sits up there, but there is a power, a fantastic power that controls us; and prayer allows us to plug into that power, especially prayer with a lot of people together.' Dorothy smiled mischievously, perhaps recognising the contradiction within her argument. She then tried to explain herself more clearly. 'I think this power is very strong. It's very personal, and you can feel it all around you. I believe there is a God. I believe that he's compassionate and full of love, and that he gives us a life to lead. We all have our ups and downs but, if we live by his code, we can deal with anything that's dished out to us.... All of us have traumas of one kind or another. I mean, the woman next door has got bad nerves; that's her trauma. I think we're all dealt problems, but if we go by the Bible and its teaching, we can get over them....'

'What about you?' I interjected.

'Well, the worst thing that can happen to me is that I die. But I've lived for 61 years and I've always felt this presence. I've always known that there was someone there, someone I could talk to, someone who could give me help and guidance. I've always felt this way....'

'Can you tell me about a situation where you experienced this strength?' I wondered aloud.

Dorothy nodded. 'When I was really ill, I never felt that I was too ill to get better. I knew that it was just a matter of time before I got better. And when I was lying there, I felt this terrific wall. I can't describe it any other way. It was like a wall all around me, and I knew that I was being cared for, being sheltered. It was just a force of love. I could feel it. I could touch it, and I knew that I was going to be all right....'

Recently, a friend of Dorothy's had also suffered a serious illness. During an acute phase of his illness, he experienced the same wall of strength surrounding him. Dorothy commented, 'We both think this strength is the presence of God. Now I think it's within us all if we just allow it to come out. That little bit of God in us is life itself, and we're not much good without life, are we?'

Since her diagnosis, Dorothy's life had changed. She had learned to cope with the physically debilitating effects of disease and the emotional trauma and challenge of long-term illness. She talked about the impact of her illness.

'I can get over the sickness and diarrhoea, and I can accept it when my mouth is bad and I can't eat. Those things are awful at the time, but when there's no alternative, I just put up with it. One of the hardest things for me to accept was losing my hair.' Dorothy smiled as though she was enjoying a secret memory. After a few moments, she turned to face me and announced, 'I think with a man, it isn't noticeable, but with a woman, it looks grotesque. I suppose it comes down to vanity. But one Sunday morning, I got up and I had hair. I went upstairs and washed it in the hand-basin, and the next minute it was all in the sink.' She grimaced.' If it had come out a little bit at a time, it wouldn't have been so bad. But it all came out at once. It was a terrific blow. But it's growing again now.' Dorothy patted her turban happily.

I cautioned Dorothy that, because of the effects of the chemotherapy, her new hair might be different in colour and in texture from her original hair. 'It's sometimes much darker when it comes back.'

She chuckled at my unnecessary warning and announced, 'Well the new hair is very white! Anyway, I used to colour it and so I never knew what shade it was! But the colour doesn't worry me as long as it's hair; that's all that matters. Of course, I'll lose it all again when I have the transplant....'

Dorothy's main concern about alopecia was its potential to shock and disgust her grandchildren. Fortunately, when she did lose her hair, they were largely unaffected. Amy, her 13-year-old granddaughter, responded with maturity. When the two met, Amy complemented her 'nannie' on how well she looked in both her wig and her turbans. Nigel, the 5-year-old grandson, was different.

'But I was wondering how my grandson would react, because he's younger.'

'And how did he react?' I encouraged.

'Well, I've seen him trying to peep under the hat here.' Dorothy pointed to the centre of the turban where a small piece of scalp was exposed. 'He was trying to see what was going on underneath. But it's strange, he's never commented on it.' She smiled. 'I remember near the beginning of the treatment, we had a chat. He was sitting on my lap at the time, munching a biscuit. He said to me, "Are you losing *all* your hair, nannie?" "Yes, darling," I said. He thought for a minute or two and then said, "So you'll look like the swimmer then?" "Yes, I suppose I will!" I said. He said, "Oh, nannie, how funny!"' As she recounted the conversation, Dorothy's face became animated. Then, becoming serious again, she added, 'But I wouldn't like them to see me ill with a bald head. I don't think there's any point. Anyway, I want them to remember me as a grandmother who laughed with them, not as a grandmother without hair....'

The family continued to dominate our conversation as Dorothy described how each member had played an important supportive role in her illness. Unable to perform her normal family roles after her diagnosis, she had relinquished her family duties and, to her delight, these had been taken over by her sons and their wives.

In retrospect, Dorothy viewed her illness as a warning. It had caused each of the family members to reconsider their relationships within the family and their dependence upon one another. Certainly, Dorothy had a new appreciation of her own dependence upon her family, particularly her dependence upon Tom.

'While I was ill having treatment, I depended on Tom completely. He did everything for me, my washing and ironing, everything. He wondered if I was eating, and he was coming back and forth to the hospital. I've always organised him and done everything for him.' She paused and grimaced. 'I may have been a bit of a bossy-boots and not allowed him to do anything, but suddenly we reversed our roles and he had to start caring for me.'

'How did you feel about that?' I challenged.

'Well, as you know, the treatment isn't very pleasant,' she replied, 'and really, I was glad that I'd got someone that I could lean on and rely on, which I could with him and the rest of them. My sons have come out of this very well, and I think that they might be a little closer with their families because of this. Now they realise how much the mother keeps the stability of the home.' She paused. 'In the past, I've always seen to everything. If anything went wrong in the family, they came to me and I sorted it out. Then suddenly I needed sorting out. But they were able to cope and that's the important thing....'

Dorothy sat in silence for a few moments and then remarked philosophically, 'When I grew up, everyone had problems, and now our family is the same. It's a part of living: you learn from whatever happens to you. You learn from your mistakes.' Dorothy grunted and then admitted, 'This has made me realise what a big mistake Tom and I made in saving for a rainy day. We were a bit stupid to save so much, but it goes back to the old days, of being brought up in conditions where you were destitute if you didn't have a pound in your pocket. We make up for it now. No, when you're young, you should spend money on holidays, going abroad and not worry too much about being secure.... Possessions aren't important either. The only thing that is important is that you have a home where, when you open the door, they're pleased to see you. A home where you know that they're behind you all the way.'

'So really it's your family relationships that have helped you to cope with the illness?' I concluded.

Dorothy nodded. 'Yes. When I was ill, very ill, the family would come in to see me, and I wasn't really with it. I slept a lot and I didn't really care where I was. But once I started getting better, I wanted to go home. That first month, I was in hospital for 3 weeks, and I began to feel that I was never coming home.... When I finally came back, I walked in here and looked around me and I realised how lucky I was

3. DOROTHY

to have this place!' Dorothy smiled. 'I suppose I was surprised that the family rallied so well! I didn't expect it. It's one of the nice things about the illness: I realise that the family has become very, very close...and all my neighbours and friends....' She hesitated and frowned. 'There's only my one niece who hasn't been in contact with us. She's 37. We can only think that she's scared of catching something, scared of catching cancer....'

* * *

2 months later, Dorothy was admitted to hospital. Her long wait had finally ended. She was scheduled to receive her transplant on 27 October.

The procedure was successful and, after 4 weeks in isolation, Dorothy was allowed home to convalesce. Shortly after her discharge home, I telephoned Dorothy and arranged to meet her again. We set a date in November.

18 November 1987

Once again, we were in the lounge of the Williams's home, seated either side of the gas fire. A few rays of late autumn sunshine filtered through the windows. There was a strong south-westerly wind and, as I looked out of the window, I could see leaves scuttling across the grass and I could hear the gnarled branches of an apple tree tapping and scraping at the slatted wooden fence at the bottom of the garden.

I asked Dorothy about her transplant. 'Tell me about your experiences on the unit. What was it like?'

'Well, it seemed forever,' Dorothy began. 'At first, it wasn't too bad, but then I became too ill to occupy my mind with reading and things, and I missed not chatting to people. The nurses came in to see to me, and my husband and my sister visited me, but we weren't allowed to touch one another and I got a bit lonely. The food was terrible as well. It was all tinned, and I never eat tinned food at home. While I was on the treatment, I couldn't eat because of the sickness, but once I began to get better I was very hungry...' Words came tumbling out of Dorothy's mouth in a stream of consciousness. 'It's too early yet to say that it's definitely taken, but everything's going in the right direction. It was lovely coming home, as well. I never realised how much home meant to me. I think it gives me a security.' She paused and pulled gently at the front of her turban, adjusting its position on her forehead.

'It must feel strange just before you come out,' I proposed.

'Yes,' she affirmed. 'I felt a bit frightened.'

'In what way?' I asked.

'Well, I was leaving the unit and the security of the nurses there.... I'd been looking forward to coming home for days and then, just before I left, I began to wonder if I could cope with it all. But as soon as I walked in here and sat down, it was OK.' Dorothy smiled and made a wide sweeping gesture with her arm, a gesture that took in the whole room. 'It was very rewarding....'

'It must have...' I started, but Dorothy interrupted me. 'It was like when they said to me, "You're going to have the transplant tomorrow." I built it up into something important, which it wasn't. It was just a transfusion. But I sat there, watching it go back in. It smelled terrible, like rotten sweetcorn, and I smelled of it for two or three days.' She paused. 'It was most peculiar watching it go in, because I knew that it was a part of me that had been taken away and was being put back, and I knew that everything depended on it. It was very traumatic, although in itself it was just another blood transfusion.... The nurses realised how important it was too; they were very careful when they handled it.' Dorothy laughed as she added, 'Well, there's not much of it. I think I only had about a litre....' She sat back in her chair and exclaimed, 'I still find it amazing to think that it's still alive, that it's a living thing and that it grows again. It's incredible! But the treatment's new, and I was very apprehensive, because...' Dorothy turned towards me, her normally jolly face downcast and serious. 'Do you remember Dave?' she asked.

I nodded. 'Yes!'

'The day I started chemo, I found out that Dave had died. It put me off my balance a bit, because he was such a strong person, mentally and, I thought, physically. He helped me tremendously in the way I thought about things, about being positive.... As I told you, I've had this terrific strength all the way through my treatment. But it wasn't as strong on the transplant unit. I don't know if it was Dave's death,

3. DOROTHY

because that really shook me, but somehow I didn't feel so closely guarded....'

'Can you describe those feelings?' I enquired.

'I broke my heart for the first day.' Dorothy confessed. 'Well, I didn't think it would happen to Dave. Yes, I knew he was ill, but you normally get these terrible temperatures and infections after the chemo, so I thought it was that. I didn't think he would die....' Absorbed in her thoughts, it seemed as though Dorothy was working through the experience as she spoke. 'He was only 47 and he was such a great person. All the staff loved him; you could tell by the way they reacted to him. And he was always so good with the other patients, with people like me. He always said the right thing and did the right thing. He was so encouraging.'

'Did Dave's illness make you question whether to go ahead with your own transplant?' I suggested.

Dorothy nodded. 'Yes! I saw Dave when he was very ill with the infection, so when I saw Dr Roberts, I told him that I had doubts about the transplant, and I asked him how long I could stay in remission, now I was well.... He asked me what brought this on, and I told him that I'd seen Dave and that we'd talked.' Dorothy spoke slowly, faltering between each sentence as she struggled with her feelings surrounding Dave's death. 'In a way, I'm sorry that I found out about Dave. Possibly, it would have been better if I'd heard afterwards, but I did find out, and I've been in touch with Paula, and she's getting on all right, so there's nothing I can do about it now. I'll just have to do what I can for Paula when I'm better....' Dorothy paused for a few moments, pulled herself together and then declared, 'Before I heard about Dave, I'd got into remission, and I really thought, "I'm in control now." I really believe that a lot of it is mind over matter, and, like Dave, I think you have to be positive. You can't sit back and let everything happen to you. You must push yourself and do things according to how you feel. Your body will tell you when you've had enough and when to rest. I think you're 85% of the way there if you have a positive frame of mind.' She hesitated again before going on, 'I also saw Dr Green the other day, and he's very truthful. I asked him what would happen if this stuff didn't take. He said that I was doing very well and that they were very pleased with me, but that if it didn't take, there would be no further treatment because of my age. I said, "Back to square one!" And he said, "Not exactly square one...." That rattled my foundations a bit. I suppose they would try and keep me in remission, but I can't keep on having chemotherapy for ever more, can I?'

Although Dorothy knew the answer to her question, I felt obliged to make a comment. Embarrassed, I mumbled, 'No, you can't.'

Dorothy continued hurriedly. 'I was a bit shaken, but I've come up from that. I'm not afraid to die. I'm apprehensive, yes, but not afraid.... I've gone 61, and I've never been ill before. I've had a good childhood, a good father and mother, a good grandmother, and now I've had a good marriage....'

As Dorothy shared her thoughts, I recollected a situation on the ward when she had been confronted by death. During the early part of her illness, she had been deeply distressed by the death of two fellow patients. Normally, Dorothy was undemanding. Consequently, the staff were surprised when, on her next admission to the ward, Dorothy refused to stay in the room where the two women had died. I wondered whether the combination of Dave's death and her conversation with Dr Green had revived Dorothy's fear of death, confronting her with the truth of her own potential death? If so, could she share her burden with anyone? Could she, for instance, talk to Tom? Later in our conversation, these questions were partially answered.

'...I don't talk about death with Tom, because he's too emotional. I talked to him about my meeting with Dr Green and what he told me, and we decided that we knew that that was going to happen, but it wasn't going to happen just yet.' She went on quickly, 'I'm hoping that the treatment will be successful and that we get extra time.... I was a bit depressed for a few days after I saw him. But I've got used to it and, anyway, we've all got to die sometime. Some people die as they're getting off the bus or they get knocked down; at least we've had a warning and we can prepare ourselves.'

Dorothy sat and stared at the fire. She was silent and motionless as she watched the tiny, dancing flames. Suddenly, she turned towards me and asked abruptly, 'Would you like some tea?'

I nodded. 'Yes please.'

Carefully, Dorothy poured the tea into two china tea-cups. With her free hand, she supported the lid of the tea-pot. Her hands shook as she handed me a cup, and, for the first time, I realised how weak Dorothy was after her transplant. Nevertheless, she was a strong and resolute woman. Striving to regain her independence, Dorothy constantly drove herself to overcome fatigue and infirmity. Indeed, as we drank our tea, she told me how, after her discharge from the unit, she had crawled up the stairs on her hands and knees. Not wanting to 'use the downstairs loo', she had been determined to use the bathroom on the first floor. Recognising Dorothy's desire for health and autonomy, I wondered whether she found it difficult talking about her illness?

Dorothy confirmed my assumption. 'No, I don't like to. I mean, it's all the same thing, over and over again. When I was ill, people would phone and they'd want to know all about it. They meant well, but I got fed up with it. In the end, I just used to say, "Oh, I'm quite well, really." I couldn't be bothered to go into details. In fact, even now, when I'm on my own, I often take the phone off the hook.' She giggled as she pretended to pick an imaginary phone off the hook. As an afterthought, she added, 'I know that's being antisocial. But as time goes on, I don't want to think about the illness and I forget what happened to me. Soon I won't remember the unit and how I spent my time. I won't remember waking up in the morning when I was well and thinking, "What am I going to do today?" Dorothy made a face. She looked bored and petulant.

'You found it boring?' I commented.

'Yes!' she confessed, 'very boring! But the nurses were good. They played Scrabble with me. They seemed to realise that it was difficult for me being in that small room, where I couldn't walk. If you're anywhere else, even if you're ill, you can walk to the toilet. But in that small room, there was nowhere to walk, only the space between the bed and the chair and the wash-hand basin.' She paused. 'I tried to do exercises every day, even if it was only lying on the bed and moving my arms and legs up and down. But there were days when I was too ill to do even that!'

'Do you remember much about those days?' I encouraged.

'No, I don't,' she replied, 'I think I was ill for about 5 days. I remember Dr Wilson coming in to see me, and he was very kind.' She paused for a moment, then, speaking slowly and purposefully, she added, 'I suppose the one who did surprise me most was Dr Green. Normally, he's so sombre but, on the unit, he was very gentle and kind. He gave me confidence. He talked quietly to me and told me not to worry –

he knew I wasn't feeling well, but he'd get to the bottom of it; and I knew he would. He was good to have around, and I found him a great comfort, which is rather surprising because I was always rather afraid of him.... But it was hard on the unit, the isolation. OK, when I'm ill, I just want to lie in bed or sit in a chair. But when I'm well, I want to do things and I want to be able to see people. It's not like Rhiannon, where there's always something happening. On the unit, there's nothing to see. I couldn't see anybody.... Yes, I could shout to the other patients. I used to shout to Graham across the way and to Enid.' She chuckled reminiscently. 'Enid didn't shout; it was mainly Graham and me!'

During her time on the unit, Dorothy had developed a close relationship with Graham. A married man with two young children, Graham was unable to cope with the isolation. Accustomed to an outdoor life and not interested in reading or writing, his only means of escape was watching television. Consequently, from early morning until late at night, he immersed himself in the sights and sounds of his television world. Having realised his dilemma, Dorothy spent many hours chatting to him. She also accepted the intrusive sound of his television without complaint. When she wanted to sleep, she simply donned her Sony Walkman headphones in order to block out the sound. Dorothy described Graham's circumstances.

'He found the isolation very difficult. He was a great big, virile chap, and he hated that small room. He was like a caged animal all the time. I often heard him, pacing around his bed. He used to talk about it. We'd pull our chairs up to the opening and chat. I remember the day Enid went home; we were both very upset. We were jealous, envious, all the things we shouldn't have been. But we didn't tell anybody until the following morning.' Dorothy chuckled again. 'I said to Graham, "I feel awful, but I was terribly jealous last night! I was envious!" He said, "Yes, I was too!" So we both felt exactly the same.... Enid was 2 weeks ahead of me, and she stayed in for 8 weeks, so actually, she was a bit slow. I was a week ahead of Graham, and my counts came up a bit quicker than his. It's funny, we used to shout our blood counts to one another and compete.' She glanced at me, checked my reaction to this and then added, 'It was in good spirit.... When I went home, Graham hid behind his curtains. He didn't want to see me go....'

Dorothy's friendship with Graham continued following her discharge from the transplant unit. They phoned each other regularly and met occasionally at the outpatient clinic. The clinic was also a place where Dorothy developed and renewed many other friendships: friendships with other transplant patients, their family members and the clinic staff. Dorothy benefited from these friendships enormously. They offered her both practical help and moral support. For example, following her transplant, Dorothy's skin became dry and encrusted. Dorothy hated her 'elephant skin'. One morning, as she sat in the clinic waiting-room, she shared her problem with the wife of another patient. When she had finished telling her story, the woman recommended a certain hand-cream. Later, Dorothy implemented the cream with great success. Dorothy described clinic life.

'I've found that all the transplant patients are very close. It's like a club. I meet people I don't know, and I meet people who've had it much longer. It's interesting, meeting them. They're all very happy and, so far, all the ones who were done about the same time as me are successful.'

'You enjoy going back to the hospital for the routine appointments?' I suggested.

'I don't like going back to Rhiannon,' Dorothy disclaimed hastily. 'I miss Sister Jones, and I don't know any of the staff there any more. At one time, it was home from home, but the atmosphere isn't the same any more.... No, I don't like going back to Rhiannon. I feel...' she paused, labouring to find words that echoed her feelings, 'I feel that a very important part of my life isn't there any more. The clinic is nice because they're always the same staff down there and they're very friendly. I usually see the same people, and they're the ones I have something in common with. So I have a good natter with them, which is nice....'

'Do you talk about your illness?' I asked.

'It depends,' she answered contemplatively. 'If it's somebody I know, we don't talk about illness. We've got other things to talk about. But last time I went in, I met a gentleman who'd had his transplant about 12 months ago. Now, we did talk about the result and how it affected him. The family were hoping that everything would be all right, and they didn't see why it shouldn't be.... So, under those circumstances, I do talk about the illness.'

Looking back over the last 7 months, I wondered how the illness had influenced Dorothy. Had she changed? Did she feel a different person?

Dorothy sat in silence, reflecting upon my questions. 'Well, I'm more tolerant now,' she remarked philosophically. 'But I don't think it's changed me. I still like the same things, like cooking and eating....' She smiled. 'The things that I thought would affect me, like losing my hair and my eyebrows, don't worry me. If people want to look, they can look. Sexually, it hasn't made any difference to me, either. Well, I'm old enough not to be interested in sex any more, but I don't know how it affects the younger ones. I should think it would.... But how has it changed me?' Dorothy repeated the phrase, reminding herself of the question. 'Well I'm much more tolerant now. I can stand back and look at things from all angles, which I couldn't do before.' In order to illustrate her new tolerant nature, she described her reaction to a controversial documentary programme that had been televised the previous week. 'I was surprised at myself!' She chuckled. '12 months ago, I wouldn't have been able to do that. I'd have been up there demanding justice, but this time I was able to sit back and consider the other alternatives....'

'Have other people commented on your changed attitude?' I asked.

Dorothy shook her head. 'No,' she exclaimed, 'because I haven't seen many people! When I was in remission, I did see people. But then I had 3 months of chemotherapy before I went down to the unit, and I didn't see anyone during that time. So, since May, I've largely been isolated from people. It seems such a long time....' Dorothy sighed deeply and then announced, 'Never having been ill before – I'd been in hospital for babies and things – it took a lot of getting used to, being ill and being unable to do things. I've been ill for nearly 7 months now. It's a long time....'

'And a lot has happened to you in that time,' I sympathised.

Dorothy nodded her head vigorously. 'Umm! A tremendous amount. But emotionally, it's been harder for Tom than for me. He's always argued that I was the stronger one. He used to say, "Oh, I'll never be left on my own because you'll live until you're 80!" My mother is 87, and she still comes in and does the housework and the laundry for me!' Dorothy smiled. 'She still thinks I'm a little girl.' Pretending to be her mother, Dorothy wagged her finger at me and said in a shaky, high-pitched voice, '"Now, Dorothy, you do what the doctor tells you."' Then becoming serious again, she murmured, 'But it's completely shaken Tom. There were many times during the treatment when he felt that he was going to be left on his own, and I don't think he could cope. While I was in hospital, he lived on his own, and he hated it....'

Dorothy sat back in her chair and stared at the fire, lost in her thoughts. 'I was very worried about him, particularly in the beginning. I was worried about his state of mind, whether he would have an accident when he was driving the car. I didn't want him to know the extent of my illness. I wanted to protect him. But when I talked to Sister Jones, she said that he had to be told and that she would involve him in care, which she did, and it worked.... Now, Tom does all the dressings and flushes the lines and, in doing those things, he feels that he's helping. He feels that he's essential to my recovery, which of course he is.... Many times, when things were bad, he'd take my hand and say, "Together we'll get there. You know that, don't you?"'

'How was it on the unit?' I interjected.

'I think he found it difficult.' Dorothy conceded. 'If I was being sick, he couldn't come in. He just had to sit there on the other side of the screen and watch. He felt helpless. He also found it hard not being able to touch me. Well, we both missed not touching.' She smiled again. 'If I wasn't feeling well on the ward, Tom and I would just catch hold of one another's hand, and we'd both get a comfort from it.' She grunted. 'We just took it for granted....'

Instead of pursuing the issues that Dorothy had raised, I changed the direction of the conversation and asked, 'Did you ever question your illness, Dorothy?'

'No!' she refuted. 'I never questioned why I was ill. I never asked, "Why me?" I never did that. I never questioned with Dave either. I think someone is in charge of all this, and it was Dave's time.... I suppose I'm surprised at the strength I've had; I'm surprised that I've been able to face up to the treatment so well, and I don't think I've been much trouble. I certainly tried not to be!'

Dorothy spoke slowly, pausing for long periods between each sentence as though she was examining her beliefs and feelings for the first time. 'It's made a much fuller person of me in as much as I now know that I'm capable of doing things, and that includes death.... I've never faced up to death before. Yes, I was aware of it, and I'd thought about it, but this has made me realise that I could cope with it as well.... I think that part of the strength I have felt has been a peace. Right through the illness, I really have had a peace of mind. I don't think there's any point in saying to yourself, "Why me? Why have I got leukaemia? I've never done anybody any harm." But I suppose I can handle it because it's me. I don't know how I'd cope if it was my child that had leukaemia. How can you explain it? You wouldn't have peace of mind, would you?'

'You wouldn't have peace of mind?' I repeated.

'No,' Dorothy affirmed. 'None at all. And peace of mind is so important, so important. It's more important than health, money, everything. Without peace of mind, you've got nothing....'

'What gives you peace of mind?' I enquired.

'Prayer,' she replied simply. 'Prayer gives me peace of mind. If I think I've done something wrong or I've hurt somebody by saying something I shouldn't, it worries me. But if I pray and I acknowledge that I've been bitchy, it helps. It gives me comfort.... I try to forgive other people as well. I'm like my mother in that respect.' Dorothy's face softened as she described her mother's life, and how her mother's philosophy and faith had influenced her own life. 'In fact,' she laughed, 'I think it's my mother's part of my nature that kept me going through the illness....'

Unlike her mother, however, Dorothy continued to struggle with doubts regarding Christianity. Although her faith had grown during her illness, her beliefs remained muddled and uncertain. Dorothy believed in God, nevertheless; she desired a closer relationship with him; she desired the richness of life associated with a strong faith. Citing the Salvation Army, a group of people known for their altruism and their acts of love and kindness to others, she identified their faith and happiness. As she spoke, I concluded that Dorothy coveted a faith like theirs.

Suffering encompasses pain in every area of life, including physical, emotional, psychological and spiritual distress. Realising Dorothy's confusion about her beliefs, I asked her if she felt that she had suffered during her illness.

'Have I suffered? she mused. 'No, I don't think I've suffered. OK, the chemotherapy isn't a pleasant treatment, but...'

'You think that suffering is a physical thing?' I interjected.

'No,' she declared, 'I think that it's a mental thing as well as a physical thing. But I certainly haven't suffered mentally and, with physical suffering, I think it must be a tremendous amount of pain that you can't cope with and, no, I haven't had that.'

I was surprised by Dorothy's response. Over the preceding months, I had seen her experience episodes of acute physical discomfort, and I had seen her go through profound periods of depression. Lately, I had also witnessed her spiritual pain, her doubt and uncertainty as she wrestled with unanswered questions regarding her faith. Recognising that it was still close to Dave's death, I wondered whether I had perhaps touched on a sensitive area. I began to feel uncomfortable and embarrassed. I also realised that Dorothy was becoming tired and so I decided that it was time to end our conversation. In an attempt at closure, I asked Dorothy if she had any plans for the future and also asked her what advice she would offer someone who had been newly diagnosed as having leukaemia.

'What are my plans for the future? Well I hope that things go well and that I stay in remission. And what do I want to do? Well, I just want to be around the house and go out occasionally for day trips with Tom, that's all.'

'Simple, everyday things,' I observed.

'Yes!' she affirmed. 'I want to go out in the park with the dog, go out to the Vale for a pub-lunch and a walk along the coastal path, nothing very exciting. And what would I recommend to others?' She considered my second question. 'I think the main thing is not to ask "Why me?" because it is you, and it's not going to go away.... You've just got to get up, look it in the face and go along with what the doctors tell you to do. God is helping you, and if it's his will, you'll get better. You've just got to face-up to it and give it all you've got, by fighting it. The last thing to do is sit around feeling sorry for yourself. I found that it helped saying the word "cancer" and getting used to saying it. At one time, if people said "cancer" you automatically thought that you were going to die, but that's not the case any more. The treatments are good and lots of people are cured!'

Knowing Dorothy's interest in counselling and her desire to help others, I asked, 'Would you like to go back and counsel patients? Go back and talk to them, tell them about your experiences?'

'Yes, I would like to,' she acknowledged. 'I'd like to provide them with some information, share my experience and reassure them that things can be done.' She smiled and added, 'But not just yet....'

* * *

In June 1988, 8 months after her transplant Dorothy continued to make good progress. In a letter, she wrote of her thoughts and feelings regarding her time of illness:

> *My blood is normal in every way and there is no trace of leukaemia at all. It is early days yet, but I am very well and I am very grateful to all the knowledge and dedication that was shown to me....*

In retrospect, Dorothy recognised the many ways in which she had benefited from her illness. She realised how illness had served to unite her family, how it had enabled her to develop new friendships with the staff and patients on the ward and how it had expanded and deepened existing friendships within the local community. Illness had also changed her as a person; it had allowed her to mature and grow. Finally, and most importantly, it had also allowed her a new experience of God.

> *I felt that my God was here near me, bringing me peace of mind. I felt that I could face anything with his presence, I felt his love and guidance. I feel sure that I have been near my God and he has been with me giving me a strength that I did not know that I had within me. I hope and pray that I will never lose this feeling. I could not live without it.*

Postscript

Sadly, Dorothy died on 10 March 1990. In a letter dated 6 September 1992, Tom wrote:

> *After the successful transplant in 1987, we had a happy time until 1 August 1989 when a recurrence was diagnosed by Dr Roberts. She was immediately started on chemotherapy again and had a second transplant in January 1990. The platelet count never recovered, and Dorothy passed away in the 'bubble' of a brain haemorrhage. We are still grieving for her.*

* * * * *

4. Dave

EVERYBODY LOVED DAVE. HE WAS A KIND, OUTGOING MAN: A MAN WITH A genuine interest in people, a man who loved to talk and listen to others, a man who always made others feel important when they were with him.

On the home front, Dave was a family man. He and his wife Paula had five children. The eldest child, Sean, was studying to become an accountant. The next two children, Gail and Jenny, were both nurses in London. Then came Stewart, who was in his last year at school, and finally Rebecca, who at 8 years of age was the baby of the family.

In appearance, Dave was tall and well-built with a ruddy complexion. He dressed casually but neatly and his hair, which was a mid-brown colour, was always cut short. His characteristic feature, however, was his smile. Dave had a smile for everyone.

Another characteristic feature of Dave was his love of nature. It was this love that attracted him into the nursery business. Dave owned and managed a flourishing nursery and market garden on the outskirts of the village. Roses and onions were his specialities.

It was in this context that I first met Dave. One rainy afternoon, I went to the nursery and wandered aimlessly around the six enormous greenhouses. Eventually, I decided to purchase a couple of geranium plants. Armed with my pots, I made my way to the nursery shop. Dave happened to be manning the cash register that afternoon, and after paying for the plants, I asked his advice on growing geraniums. For over 20 minutes, Dave patiently explained the vagaries of cultivating geraniums from cuttings. He had a rare gift for teaching. At the end of our conversation, I understood the gardening principles he had so carefully explained but, more importantly, I realised that he had treated me with extraordinary respect and courtesy.

Later, when Dave was diagnosed as having leukaemia, the memory of that first encounter returned to my mind. Ironically, that meeting laid the foundation for our subsequent relationship. A special bond had been created that endured throughout the period of Dave's illness, allowing a unique friendship to develop between us.

Dave was diagnosed as having leukaemia on Thursday 19 January 1987. He had no warning of his infirmity. At 2 pm, he attended the Dental Hospital to have two gum abscesses drained. 3 hours later, he found himself on the haematology ward being treated for acute myeloid leukaemia.

Typically, Dave coped well with the transition to patient life. Although shocked by the bombshell news of his diagnosis and the subsequent assault of chemotherapy, he experienced a remarkable sense of peace. In retrospect, this peace can be attributed to three factors: the united support of his family, his faith in God and his own exceptional attitude to illness.

Dave's family were a constant source of strength and encouragement. Throughout his illness, they provided essential practical and moral support. Paula, in particular, shared the burden of illness. In the weeks that followed Dave's diagnosis, she assumed many of the family responsibilities. In addition, she adopted the role of care giver, helping Dave with his personal needs, providing him with special meals and bullying and cajoling him when his spirits were low.

Thankfully, Gail and Jenny also provided a great deal of support. On their days off they returned home to help their parents. Interestingly, they became the family encouragers. For example, when Dave began chemotherapy, he lost his hair. To alleviate the tension surrounding his alopecia, they utilised humour. One weekend, they sat down with their father and tried to work out an artistic design that would highlight the phrens on his scalp. Within minutes, the three of them 'were roaring with laughter'. Later, as the treatment progressed and Dave lost weight, the girls again adopted humour. Dave accepted their jokes gratefully.

> *Because I've lost all my weight and my bones stick out, I've been called everything from the Sacred Cow to Gandhi. When the weather was nice, I had shorts on and these sandals and dark glasses and a bald head, and they thought that I looked like Gandhi. But I think that it's important to keep a sense of humour about things. You've got to treat things lightly, rather than get all miserable about them....*

Despite their seemingly frivolous attitude, Dave's illness had a profound impact on the children. Principally, the boys took it hard. Paula realised the pain they were suffering when they began to use a lot of swear words at home. She heard swear words that she didn't even know existed, especially from Stewart. Rebecca was also deeply affected. Initially, she accepted her daddy's illness without comment; however, after several weeks of chemotherapy, she'd had enough. On one occasion she said to her daddy, 'I don't want you to be ill any more. I want you to be better!'

Dave's spiritual support began soon after his admission to Rhiannon Ward. Still reeling from the news of his leukaemia, he sat on his bed, wondering what to do. He happened to find a copy of the Gideons' New Testament that had been placed on top of his bedside locker. He opened the Bible at Mark 5:25 and began to read.

> A large crowd followed and pressed around him. And a woman was there who had been subject to bleeding for 12 years. She had suffered a great deal under the care of many doctors and had spent all she had, yet instead of getting better, she grew worse. When she heard about Jesus, she came up behind him in the crowd and touched his cloak, because she thought, 'If I touch his clothes, I will be healed.' Immediately her bleeding stopped and she felt in her body that she was freed from her suffering.

As Dave read about the healing, his faith grew. He felt an empathy with the woman, and he knew then that he did believe in Jesus and that he would have 'not the same sort of cure but the same sort of help'.

Dave's relationship with God slowly deepened as he progressed through treatment. Each morning, as he set aside time to read his Bible and to pray, he was able to overcome the fears and anxieties that assaulted his mind. He received solace and he was given the strength he needed 'to get through the day'.

In addition to the support he received from his family and his faith, Dave assumed responsibility for his own illness and took an active role in his recovery. Convinced that the success of the treatment was dependent upon his own attitude, he was determined to do everything he could to overcome his leukaemia.

> I'm a great believer in mind over matter. I think if you've got the right attitude of mind, it definitely affects the body's own recuperative

powers. Obviously, with something like this, it has got to be treated with chemicals, but the person has got a great part to play.... When I wake up in the morning now, I have a period of about 30 minutes to myself, and during that time, I think about all the positive things to do with leukaemia. If I'm on antibiotics, I think about the antibiotics doing their job, and doing their job well. I might say a few prayers to myself.... So about half-an-hour each morning is devoted to positive thinking and getting over this disease.

Dave's endeavour to control his illness was not limited to positive thinking: he was also an active participant in care and treatment. In this regard, he opted to become a partner in care. Totally committed to the treatment, he joined forces with the professional staff and fought his illness with them. Seeking to play his part, he sought to obey the staff in every detail of treatment. He did everything he was told. He adhered strictly to the treatment regimes, performing his daily tasks, like temperature recording and mouth and skin checks, religiously, and he attended every outpatient appointment. Furthermore, he followed the doctor's advice and tried to keep himself fit by eating carefully and exercising as much as possible.

Not surprisingly, he experienced profound feelings of guilt when he failed to comply with the instructions he had been given, thereby jeopardising his treatment. For instance, while playing football at home with his dogs, he accidentally injured his toe. An infection developed and this delayed his chemotherapy by several weeks. The memory of this innocent accident haunted Dave for the rest of his life.

The one thing that did make me cross was my toe. I was absolutely furious with myself, because it was totally self-inflicted. I could blame no one else. There I was sitting on the bed with my flaming toe in front of me....

As a partner in care, Dave needed knowledge. Indeed, he liked to be well informed (but not too well informed!) so that he could contribute effectively in practical aspects of care and participate in decision-making regarding future therapy. Although Dave gleaned a lot of helpful information from the staff, his main tutors were his colleagues. Accordingly, as his own illness progressed and he gained expertise, becoming proficient in practical skills and gaining an understanding of the disease process, he was able to counsel newly diagnosed patients. Because of his easy manner, the members of staff soon began to invite him to counsel his colleagues. Then as his confidence grew, he started to counsel other patients of his own volition. On one occasion, for instance, Dave was sitting in the day room. On the opposite side of the room, a woman began to cry.

> *The tears were running down her face and dripping off her chin. I wondered if she wanted to stay by herself or if she wanted to talk about it. I thought about how I should approach her. Perhaps she didn't want anyone interfering.... In the end, I think I said something like, 'Is it bad news or something?' (Dave laughed.) Then she came on, and I couldn't stop her talking. She was talking all the time. At the end, she said to me, 'At least I know there is light at the end of the tunnel....'*

Dave believed strongly in the benefits of counselling. In particular, he was convinced of the need for counselling after the initial shock of diagnosis.

> *Initially you're in shock. That lasts for about 4 or 5 days, and during that time, everything goes to pieces. But you can put it together again, and if you can, you can get up fighting. I think you have this inbuilt mechanism which helps you to cope. Initially there's a terrific feeling of panic and disaster. Then, after about 4 or 5 days, that feeling goes and the reality sinks in and you can say 'Right, I'm going to fight it and that's that.' Obviously, if you sink into despair after the first 4 or 5 days, you're not going to fight.*

Illness changed Dave's life. As he progressed through treatment and spent time in hospital, he realised a new sensitivity, a heightened awareness. He noticed the change when he was discharged home.

> *The first time I went out of here, it was only after 5 days, and I found everything very bright and colourful and very fast-moving. As I sat in the car, I thought 'I'm going too fast' and I hung on to the seat.*

Gradually, Dave's perception of speed and colour returned to normal; nevertheless, he remained sensitive and appreciative of special events and special moments in time.

> *Now I find that I'm looking and appreciating things more. I mean, when I see a child laughing and running down the road, I think 'That's nice!' I see things in a different light. I appreciate life in a different way.... I think I'm learning to live each day as it is. Like, I appreciate the colour of flowers. Before flowers were flowers, and the colour didn't really*

4. DAVE

matter, but now the colour does matter. Everything is more pronounced and I appreciate things more....

Dave took great delight in the simple, everyday things that he formerly took for granted. As his illness progressed, his desire for normal life became focussed on these seemingly unimportant things. In order to motivate his fight against leukaemia, he began to set himself short- and long-term goals. These goals invariably encompassed an aspect of normal life that had been lost through illness.

After my first stay in hospital, it was important for me to do everything that was normal. People couldn't understand why I wanted to be normal.... I particularly wanted to go out to the pub and have a pint, because it was a normal thing to do. Once I'd done that, I was OK. The next thing, we've got a caravan in West Wales, and I set my sights on going down there. I was determined to go down, and we did.

In between his courses of treatment, Dave was discharged home to convalesce. Although he felt tired and run-down, he was determined to lead a normal life. When he was ill, Dave had no objection to being in hospital and being a patient; however, when he was well, he tried to dissociate himself from the disease and live normally.

Unfortunately, Dave could never forget that he had leukaemia. As the cycles of chemotherapy and the subsequent infections progressed, the marks of illness deepened. He displayed the physical changes associated with the disease and its treatment, such as weight loss, skin discoloration and ulceration, loss of concentration, taste changes and alopecia. Even in between the cycles of chemotherapy, the stigma lingered. Extreme weakness and fatigue and the visible signs of disease were a constant reminder of his condition. Interestingly, however, it was the subtle physical changes that caused Dave the most distress.

I've lost my eyebrows and my eyelashes, so when I'm out in the sun, my eyes water tremendously. Normally, when you frown, your eyebrows protect your eyes from the sun; but they don't with me. I've got to wear sunglasses all the time, even in normal light. The hairs in my nose have gone too. Normally, when you breathe through your nose, the hairs filter out the dust and make the air a little bit warmer. Well of course, with me, the air is going straight through to the mucous, and so I have a permanent drip on the end of my nose. It's the little things like that which

> *I found made a difference. The little things I wasn't expecting which suddenly seem to bring it home that I've got leukaemia.*

Accordingly, Dave resented the loss of his social life: his inability to work or go to a rugby match with his friends, his inability to garden or swim or go to church. Essentially, he resented the loss of his independence and liberty, the loss of his personal future.

Feeling strangely helpless and fearful of becoming a burden to his family and friends, Dave nursed a hidden sense of anger and frustration. Occasionally, when family members were overprotective and threatened his independence even further, his emotions were uncovered and he erupted in anger.

The words cancer and leukaemia are analogous with the concept of a curse or stigma. In order to confront illness, Dave had to overcome the fear associated with his illness label. To achieve this, he decided to take an aggressive position and face his disease, participating actively in the treatment and care and developing a positive mentality.

Fear associated with illness has the potential to form a barrier, isolating and alienating the person from others. When Dave had overcome his own fear of illness, he was then able to address that same fear in others. To do this he endeavoured to expose his illness, whenever possible.

> *If people come and appear to be a little bit afraid of the word, then I say it for them. I say, 'Look, I've got leukaemia, and I'm going to make the most of it!' They seem to be able to relax a little bit then, and instead of having a stilted conversation, where they try and talk around it, we can talk openly. It might be a shock to start with, but it bears fruit in the long run.*

Nevertheless, as the date for the transplant drew nearer, Dave withdrew into himself. He became preoccupied with thoughts of the transplant and the time of isolation. Inevitably, all the family shared in the tension. At home, emotions were raw, and arguments between members of the family were not uncommon. Aware of Dave's situation, I arranged to see him in his home, shortly before his admission to the radiotherapy unit. This would be our third formal interview together.

27 June 1987

It was a warm summer afternoon. Dave and I sat facing each other across an elegant glass-topped coffee table in the dining room at the rear of the house. Dave was dressed in a pair of light-weight summer trousers and a short-sleeved cotton shirt. He looked tanned and fit; he had obviously put on a few pounds in weight in preparation for the transplant. I switched on the tape-recorder and we began to chat.

Dave was eager to talk, and he immediately launched into a discussion about his thoughts and feelings regarding the transplant. In particular, he began to explore his feelings of depression.

'The last 4 or 5 weeks, I've been a bit down in the dumps. I've had to shake myself in the morning, and sometimes it takes me about half-an-hour to pull myself out of it.'

'Do you know what was causing the depression?' I ventured.

Dave nodded. 'For a long time, I'd shut the leukaemia out of my mind. I'd been a bit of an ostrich. Anyway, a couple of weeks ago, I decided that it was time I found out about it, and so I went down to the library and got out one of the medical text books. About the same time, Jenny finished work in London. She was on an oncology ward up there and so, of course, she brought her books home with her. The family didn't want me to see any of them, but I got hold of one of the books and I insisted on reading it.' He gave a wry grin. 'I was OK until the book started talking about death and there being no cure for leukaemia. Seeing it in print brought it all home to me. I was OK looking for knowledge but, when I found out certain things, I started to get a bit depressed.' He hesitated briefly. 'I think I'd built a sort of barrier around myself. I'd persuaded myself that the transplant was a cure and all the rest of it. I'd shut out that side of the illness and, by reading about it, I came back down to earth again...' He paused for a few moments, considering the situation and then added, 'Then I let myself get down. I thought, "Is it worth it all? Is it worth going through all the treatment when at the end of it, there's only a limited chance of success...?"'

'How did you deal with the depression?' I wondered aloud.

Dave grinned. 'This is where physical wellbeing comes into it,' he began. 'If I'm lying in bed in the morning and I'm depressed, I get up out of bed and I think, "Right, I'm going to clean my teeth!" So I go and do my teeth and have my mouthwash and I'm positive. Then I go downstairs and I have my morning routine all organised, and I get on with it.' Dave spoke quickly, obviously excited and totally convinced of the efficacy of his strategy. 'It's no good just sitting there feeling sorry for yourself. You've got to sort out a couple of things that you know you've got to do, and you've got to get on and do them. The worst thing that you can do is sit there and mope around. You've got to get yourself into doing something. It doesn't matter what it is. It may be cleaning your teeth, but get on and do it positively.' He paused and chuckled. 'I was going to say, "And combing your hair", but I don't have much hair any more.' He gently stroked the fine, downy hair on his head.

'Not at the moment,' I rejoined.

Dave grinned at me gratefully. 'No. But, as I was saying, you've got to do that job properly. Clean your teeth properly and make a good job of it, rather than do it halfheartedly. Then move on to the next thing. If it's dressing, then dress properly.'

'So, it's a step-by-step approach.' I reflected.

'Exactly.' Dave nodded enthusiastically. 'And it does help. It might take you half-an-hour of doing things like that, but it does pull you out of it.' He glanced at me and then confided, 'I still worry about the future, though, about the transplant. I worry that I might not be able to jump out of bed in the morning and do things, because I'm physically incapable of it. I hadn't really thought about it until now, but it does frighten me to think about that.'

'Are there other things that frighten you?' I suggested.

Dave leaned back in his chair, contemplating my question. 'I've had a few traumatic experiences in hospital.' He glanced up at me again. 'Do you remember when Lorraine died?'

I nodded in affirmation.

'Well,' he continued, 'that particular night and the following day, I worried about her death. I realised that that could happen to me, and it frightened me. Then when Ralph was bad...'

'Tell me about it,' I encouraged.

'Well, I was in the same room as him. It was a two-bedded room. Ralph was due to have a Hickman line put in, and he wasn't terribly well; his chest was "rattly". Anyway, he went down to have the line put in, and when he came out, he was particularly ill; he really went downhill. That night the staff were in and out of the room with all sorts of machines, putting tubes down his throat.' Dave turned away and stared out of the window. 'Later on, the staff moved me to another room across the corridor, but it still knocked me back. Being there, seeing all those things happen to him and knowing that he also had AML, I realised that the same sort of thing might happen to me. I suppose I should have tried to shut it out, but I couldn't. Anyway as soon as I realised that I was thinking things like that, I came to terms with myself and got on top of my thoughts. Since then, I've been in and spoken to Ralph and I've been fine.' Dave turned and grinned sheepishly at me. 'That sort of thing knocks me for six, though, like Lorraine's death. It frightens me, because it's so close to the transplant, but I'm beginning to accept it better now.'

I challenged Dave. 'In what way are you beginning to accept it?' I asked.

'I don't know,' he mused. 'I supposed I'm a bit more prepared for that to happen than I was. I suppose you do get used to things as time goes on. I mean, Lorraine's death was the first leukaemia death that had been close to me in any way. I hadn't had an experience like that before and, because I hadn't, I think it was probably more traumatic.' He paused and added, 'I know that sounds a bit callous, but I think you do get used to it after a while. You harden yourself against it and you accept it.'

I sought to clarify Dave's feelings. 'Do you harden yourself against it? Or do you block yourself off?'

Dave nodded thoughtfully. 'Yes, I think you're right. I think I do shut part of my mind off. I don't harden myself; I'm not that sort of person.' He chuckled quietly and confessed, 'It still upsets me when someone dies. It still brings tears to my eyes. I'm an emotional softy when it comes to things like that. So, yes, I do believe that I shut my mind off.'

'And how do you feel now?' I interjected.

'Better!' Dave replied succinctly.

'What brought about your change of heart?' I persisted.

'I think a number of things have helped me,' Dave began. 'I was telling you that I was a bit down in the dumps. Well something happened about 10 days ago. A friend of ours had been ill. He'd been a bit anaemic and he'd lost some blood. He was actually in hospital the same time as I was; he was in for tests. Anyway, the doctors decided that they would operate. They did, and then they closed him up straight-away. Apparently, he had a large tumour on his intestines. Later, they told him that he'd got inoperable cancer and they gave him between 2 months and 2 years to live....'

'That's hard,' I conceded.

Dave nodded. 'Alice, his wife, phoned up to speak to Paula and me. She asked, "How do you cope with this sort of thing? Do you tell the children? Do you tell other people?" We found that we were able to help them quite a lot initially. After the first 4 or 5 days, they seemed to settle to it. They could manage on their own. But being able to help them helped us. Knowing that I could help someone else helped me.'

'Did it boost your morale?' I asked.

Dave looked perplexed. 'No, I wouldn't exactly explain it that way. No, it gave me a strength, and it helped me to overcome feelings of self-pity. When I heard that he had 2 months to live, it really made me think. I began comparing their situation with ours, and I realised how lucky we were.' He paused and then went on, 'But Jim's diagnosis did scare me. And then, what with reading those books and it getting closer to my going into the transplant unit, I suddenly felt rather frightened, and I wanted to go to church again. I wanted to go because I wanted to draw on that strength.' He grinned at me and confessed, 'But at the same time, I felt guilty because I haven't been to church for quite a while; either my counts were a bit low or one of the children was home. Anyway, last Sunday, I finally went to church, and since then I've tended to get to grips with things again.' He paused momentarily and then continued, 'I find it a great help going to church, knowing that I'm not on my own. I find that it helps to keep me going; it keeps my spirits up.'

'You mentioned that you felt guilty going to church. Was that because you felt that you were using God?' I suggested.

Dave nodded slowly. 'Yes, I think so. When I was first ill, I found that faith was a great strength. Then when I got better, I wasn't quite so conscious of it. Now that I'm approaching the transplant and I'm beginning to get a little bit frightened, I turned back to church and back to faith and, yes, I did feel guilty!' He grinned mischievously at me. 'But I definitely did need to go to church.'

'You needed to go,' I echoed.

'Yes, I needed to go.' He smiled reminiscently and then said, 'Last Sunday it was a communion service and I went forward at the communion. Now, I'm not confirmed so, normally, I just go for a blessing and the vicar comes up and puts his hand on mine and then moves on. But this time he did something a little bit different. This time he put the chalice down on the altar table, and he came back and put his two hands on my head and prayed for me. The blessing that he gave me lasted about a minute and a half, which is quite a long time when you've got a full congregation there, all waiting to take communion, and this had quite a profound effect on me.'

'Can you describe what you felt like?' I asked.

'I find it difficult to describe,' he replied hesitantly, searching for the right words to explain his emotions. 'It was a feeling of wellbeing, a feeling of being filled, of not being empty any more.' He looked down at his hands and murmured, 'I've always been waiting for something to happen, for something to suddenly explode in front of me and for everything to be changed and different. I've always wanted an experience where there's a flashing light and a blaring of trumpets. But I've come to the conclusion that this will never happen to me. Instead my faith is something that will build more gradually. But that experience in church last Sunday was part of the build-up, and it has helped. I no longer have any doubts about my faith. I know I've got help and, because the help is there, the doubts that I had previously have gone completely. I've gone through a phase as far as my faith is concerned, where my faith is far more solid. It's given me a strength to fall back on.' He glanced at me and smiled. 'It sounds as if it's a crutch, doesn't it?'

I nodded in reply, thankful that he had identified his own sentiments.

'Well, it is a support. I can't find the right words to explain it, but it's a necessary support. If I wake up in the night feeling a bit frightened and a bit lonely, I've just got to pray and I'm fine. It sounds a bit selfish, but I'm able to go back to sleep.'

Instead of pursuing Dave's thoughts on his faith, I asked him about his insomnia. 'Do you often wake up?'

'Yes, I do,' he confessed. 'I think I'm getting a bit worried about the transplant. I'm not worried about being on the unit, although I'm not particularly looking forward to it, and I'm not worried about the actual radiotherapy and chemotherapy. I think it's the thought of possible side-effects from the radiotherapy and the success of the transplant that's worrying me.' He paused and then continued, 'As I explained to you, about 3 weeks ago, I began to feel a bit frightened. I think it was partly because I'd read too many of the wrong things in books and partly because I'd been to see Dr Green. He talked about the transplant and he told me that the success rate wasn't 100% and that two people hadn't done well. He didn't go into details but, anyway, I was a bit worried about that. Then I went to see Dr Roberts, and he told me about the side-effects of the radiotherapy. He told me about the cataracts forming and the skin reactions and I thought, "Oh, not something else I've got to go through."'

'It must feel as though it's never-ending,' I said sympathetically.

He shrugged his shoulders indifferently and replied, 'Yes, but, I'm determined that the transplant will be a success.' He hesitated and then added, 'I think that a lot of the success of this type of thing depends on your attitude. Now, I lapsed a little bit, but I've come to terms with things again, and I'm determined that everything is going to be successful. There's no question of anything going wrong.'

'You seem quite adamant,' I remarked.

Dave nodded. 'Well, I'm a great believer in the phrase "Physician, heal thyself." I think the way you feel has a lot of bearing upon what actually happens. If you're negative, then you'll encourage the negative things to happen. So you've got to be positive.'

'Do you find that other people's attitudes affect you?' I interjected.

'Umm!' Dave agreed. 'If I see someone not bothering to fight, it makes me more determined to fight; and if I see someone doing well, it makes me determined to do just as well; and if someone's down in the dumps, I think "Well, that's not the way to deal with it, for a start."

So yes, other people's attitudes do affect me. But regardless of their attitude, it seems to have a positive effect on me.' He paused and then went on, 'Talking to other people helps as well. When Rachel rang up this morning, it made me feel included and wanted. I knew that I wasn't alone.' By way of explanation, he added, 'Recently, I haven't been on the ward as much. And when I have been in, there hasn't been anybody else that I know. I suppose I've been a bit disappointed,' he chuckled. 'Initially when I was in, there were always four or five of us in together and we had a great time, quite hilarious.'

'There's a security with your colleagues, isn't there?' I observed.

Dave nodded seriously. 'Yes, there's a security with the patients you know, and there's also a security with the staff you know.' He hesitated and then announced, 'I think that's another reason why I wasn't looking forward to the unit. I didn't know anyone down there, and I didn't know what it was like.'

'But you visited the unit recently, didn't you?' I reminded him.

'Yes,' Dave confirmed. 'I went on Wednesday morning. And I think going to the unit, seeing one or two faces there, seeing the environment, seeing what I was going into, has made a difference. I'm less apprehensive now.' He smiled mischievously. 'I know Dr Green wasn't keen for me to go, but it has helped a lot. I'm not nearly as frightened as I was.... But,' he broke off, searching for words, 'I still think the atmosphere on the unit is one of being locked in. It would really help if something could be done about that.'

'Do you have any suggestions?' I encouraged.

'Well, if something could be done with the view from the window, it would help enormously. At the moment, there's no outlook. You don't see anything except the courtyard, a confined space, and that gives you the feeling of being trapped. I like to see a distance. If I can see trees and greenery and movement, it makes me feel better.'

'It represents freedom, doesn't it?'

'Exactly,' Dave agreed vehemently. 'It's freedom, and it makes me feel less restricted. If I can see cars moving around, I know there are people out there and I don't feel as though I'm on my own. If I can't see cars and trees, I feel isolated and lonely.' He paused again and then added as an afterthought, 'I suppose some posters on the wall would help, posters that showed a distance.' He shrugged his shoulders, carelessly, 'But I have to be positive about the transplant. I've got to go through with it, because there is no alternative.' He grinned at me, 'I have no option.'

'How do you feel about that, about knowing you only have one option?'

Dave sat in silence, quietly considering the implications of my question. 'In many ways,' he began, 'it's easier not having a choice. As a layman, it's difficult making a decision on something like that. It's hard making a decision without having all the medical knowledge.' He paused briefly and then added, 'The trouble is, as a layman, I used to worry about the transplant. I used to worry about the unknown. I wondered how I would cope with being alone for 6–7 weeks in the one room. But seeing people in there and finding out what I can take in with me has made a lot of difference. I'm not looking forward to it, but I'm not apprehensive.'

'It will be a unique experience for you,' I interposed.

'Dave gave a grunt of indifference. 'Well, I don't know. But I think I'll cope OK. I seem to be able to occupy my mind reasonably well, as long as I have things to read, like the *Daily Telegraph*.' He glanced at me and then confided, 'I am concerned about the toilets though. Initially I was told that every room had its own toilet. But they haven't; they've got commodes in them.' He laughed sardonically. 'Now it might seem a little thing to you to have to use a commode rather than a toilet, but it's something that I find not very encouraging.'

'No, it's not a very exciting prospect,' I commiserated.

'But on the whole,' he continued, 'I think I can cope with it. I mean, I coped with being in hospital for 6 weeks, although at the time, I had a lot of visitors. But I don't mind being on my own because I enjoy reading and I have a good imagination.'

'You have a good imagination,' I repeated.

'Yes,' he responded and explained. 'When I was in hospital before, I'd go for an imaginary walk every morning. I'd go out through the front door, on to the pavement, down the kerb, across the road and up the opposite kerb. Then I'd walk a specific route into the village and, once I'd got there, I'd walk back again, this time by a different route.' He grinned. 'Well, I needed my daily exercise! But going back to the isolation. I don't mind being on my own. Obviously, I may not feel the same way after 6 weeks on the Unit but, at the moment, I think it'll be harder for Paula than it will be for me.'

'Why is that?' I enquired.

'Well, I don't think she'll feel a part of it. I think she'll feel as though she's on the outside looking in, whereas I'll be in it. We've found this all the way along, and I've come to realise that it's much harder on Paula than it is on me. She has to carry a lot more strain than I do. OK, I get frightened and depressed, but she gets the strain and stress....'

Instead of pursuing this topic of conversation, I asked Dave about his thoughts for the future. 'Have you thought beyond the transplant yet?'

'Yes,' he responded. 'I mean, I've spoken to Dr Green, and as far as he's concerned, most of the patients who have had an autologous transplant are OK after 2 years. In Edinburgh, they've been doing autologous transplants longer, and patients there have gone 5 years. So yes, I have thought about the future, because we obviously have to have an income. Now I'd thought of going back to the nursery, but it just doesn't appeal any more.'

'Why is that?' I challenged.

'I don't know,' he answered uncertainly. 'I almost feel frightened of going back and doing something involved in business. This feeling has only come the last couple of days, and now I'm wondering what I can do and what I want to do.'

'Is it because you're frightened of going back or is it because the work doesn't appeal to you any more?' I asked.

Dave thought for a few moments and then said, 'I'm not frightened of going back, but I've got a vague misty feeling about this. There's something I want to do, but I don't know what it is.... Maybe it'll come to me after the transplant, after I've had time to think about it on the unit.' He paused and then confessed, 'I suppose if I knew that I had 2 years to live or 5 years, I could work out something but, at the moment, everything is so uncertain. I'm not confused about the future, but there are no clear thoughts in my mind, except that I just can't see myself going back and running another business. I've got to do something different, but I don't know what that something is.' He grinned. 'Hopefully, it will become more clear after the transplant....'

* * *

Dave went into his transplant with high hopes, determined to do everything in his power to make the transplant a success. Indeed, it didn't occur to him that 'things wouldn't work out'. Inevitably, he found the early adjustment to the unit wasn't easy. When he entered the unit, he felt claustrophobic and was unhappy about the lack of privacy. However, after the initial feelings of panic had dissipated, he soon settled into the routine and participated actively in the treatment and care, refusing to think of himself as an invalid. In his free time, Dave entertained himself by watching television, listening to tapes, talking, reading and doing the *Daily Telegraph* crossword. (During the transplant, 'doing the crossword' became a matter of principle. He had to complete the crossword by a certain time each day.) He also exercised rigorously, doing strenuous leg and arm exercises and cycling on his exercise bicycle. Ironically, Dave found that there weren't enough hours in the day to accommodate all his recreational pastimes.

Initially, the treatment went well. Dave reacted well to the radiotherapy and chemotherapy and the marrow transfusion went smoothly. Shortly afterwards, his blood counts showed that the marrow had grafted, and subsequently he was discharged home. Sadly, however, it was soon apparent that something was wrong. Dave's blood counts continued to rise rapidly and it was clear that his leukaemia had come back.

I met Dave and Paula the day after they had received the news of Dave's relapse. The sunshine of that warm Sunday afternoon seemed totally inappropriate. The sadness of our conversation was incongruous with the glorious August weather. I sat and chatted with Dave and Paula for only a short time, seeking to help them find a way through their desolation. I could do little save offer my condolences. As we parted, Dave asked me to come back a few days later to talk.

19 August 1987

The sky was grey and overcast that afternoon. Perhaps, I mused, the weather man's warning regarding the possibility of an evening thunderstorm was correct. I walked from the village towards Dave's home. As I approached the house, I thought about the time I was going to spend with Dave. I wondered what our conversation would be like and I hoped that I would be able to offer him some consolation and encouragement. A little nervously, I rang the doorbell.

A few moments later, Paula opened the door. Behind her smile of welcome, her eyes betrayed a sense of disillusionment. After directing me to the living room, she retreated into the kitchen to clear away the lunch things. When I entered the room, Dave who was resting on the sofa, rose to greet me. After we had shaken hands and hugged, he lay back on the couch while I made myself comfortable in an armchair.

As I set up my tape-recorder, I studied Dave's appearance. He seemed to have aged 10 years over the last week. His thin, drawn face was heavy with sadness and his body appeared tired and shrunken. Uncertain as to what I should say, I sat in silence. Perhaps aware of my discomfort, Dave began to explain what had happened after his discharge home.

'I came home on Tuesday last week, thinking that everything was OK. Then on Wednesday, my counts went from 1.9 to 3.9. I was delighted. I thought, "This is great. They've taken off that quickly." Then on Thursday they went to 6.2, and it was then that I began to think that things weren't going the way they should. The counts were going up too high. On the following day, when they came through at 10.2, I knew that something was wrong. It couldn't possibly have gone that high because the normal count is only between 4 and 11. Anyway on Saturday morning, we were sitting in Sister Jones's office, and Sister Jones came in with Dr Purvis, and they said that I didn't need platelets. So I said, "What's my blood count?" And they said, "14". Their faces were emotionless. Well, I knew then, and after that Dr Purvis did tell us.'

'What did he say?' I prompted.

'Well,' Dave sighed, 'prior to that, he'd told me that my counts were a bit high and that there could be an infection, which they couldn't see.' Dave hesitated and then explained, 'I didn't have a temperature you see. Anyway, he then said that it might be something more sinister. Well, I knew what he meant by "something more sinister". About half-an-hour later, he came into the treatment room while my dressing was being done and he said, "Well, I've got to tell you. The leukaemia is reverting back. You're out of remission. There is a vague chance that the lab people might find some infection that is causing it, but not really...."' Dave glanced at me and smiled. 'I don't suppose I was as shocked as all that because I was half expecting it anyway, but I just lay on the couch, holding on to Sister Jones's arm and looking out of the window and letting it all sink in. A bit later, I went out and met Paula.' His eyes glowed with reminiscence. 'Paula told me that she was determined not to cry, but she did....' Dave paused again and then said quietly, 'Once we'd got over the initial emotion of it, it wasn't too bad, but over the weekend I felt totally shattered. If I'd had 6 months before slipping out of remission, it would have been something, but to have no time at all, I thought, "It's not fair!"' He laughed bitterly. 'I know I was still in shock. Well, certainly, the whole period from Saturday to Monday seemed an awfully long time. When I was in the day unit this morning, I couldn't believe that it was only Wednesday.'

'Time disappeared, didn't it?' I observed, 'Did you feel the same when you were first diagnosed?'

'No!' Dave refuted my suggestion vehemently. 'No, that was different. When I was first diagnosed, I didn't feel down in the dumps, I just felt that it was something that was put there for me to get over and that I would get over it. This time it was different. It was as though the rug had been pulled from underneath me. I was shocked and dejected. I thought, "What's the point? Why bother?"'

'You'd worked so hard,' I commented.

'I had,' Dave agreed, 'I tried very hard. Perhaps I tried too hard.' He gave a wry grin. 'Anyway, I let myself get a bit down and, because my head got a bit fuzzy, I couldn't think straight. But today I feel quite well and my mind's clear.'

'Your mind's clear,' I reflected.

'Yes, I know what's in front of me,' he explained, 'I know what I'm going to do about it. Over the weekend, I couldn't think about anything. I thought that it was the end, that I probably had about 6 weeks and then that was it, boom-boom! But since then I've realised that I have to be more positive. I have to make things go my way again.'

'You were certainly very shocked on Sunday when I saw you,' I said.

Dave nodded. 'Yes, I think I went into my shell. I didn't want to know anything and I couldn't talk to people about it very easily.' He turned and glanced out of the window. 'I've always been very straightforward with friends. Anyway, yesterday I was talking to Elsie next door and she said, "How are you?" I said, "Fine," and she said, "Good." I thought, "No! I can't let her go on thinking that," and so I told her what had happened.'

'How did she react?' I asked.

'She was very disappointed and a little shocked. I could hear the shock in her voice, but she went on talking, and then I said, "It's one of those things. You either put up with it or you go under." After that she was talking about it quite normally.' Dave paused momentarily and then went on, 'But I haven't sorted out my thoughts and feelings yet. I know I was very confused, but I don't know if I was bitter or angry or cross. I don't think so.' He paused again. 'When I was on the unit, I kept God by my side the whole time, and I think I felt a bit selfish about it. I felt as though I was taking more than my fair share. Then when I slipped out of remission, I didn't want to think about it any more.'

'You didn't want to think about God?' I asked.

'That's right,' Dave affirmed. 'I didn't stop believing, and I was still talking to God, but I was confused. I suppose I felt cheated, very cheated, and I couldn't understand why this had happened to me. I don't think of myself as a particularly good person,' he mused, 'but I've never been a bad person and I couldn't understand why God had allowed it to happen to me...'

As we talked, Dave relaxed. Gradually, he regained a more positive outlook on his illness and the resentment he had harboured towards his colleagues dissolved. Dave commented on the change in his feelings.

'I saw Emily in the unit yesterday. When she saw me, she came up with a big smile on her face and said, "How are you?" I told her that things weren't quite right, and suddenly I felt really angry. I thought, "Why should I be the one that had things go wrong?" I mean the others haven't gone through it yet, only Emily, but I didn't want to' talk to any of them any more. Since we've been talking, though, I feel more like I used to previously.'

'In what way?' I interposed.

'Well, I feel that I can go back and talk to the other patients. I can let them say how well they're doing or whatever, and I won't mind.' He smiled at me and then went on, 'Dorothy is going to have her transplant next week. Well, Paula and I were worried about her, because she relies a lot on Dr Roberts and how other people are doing. If she'd been told out of the blue that my transplant hadn't worked, I don't know what she'd have done. Anyway, we decided that Paula would go round and tell them. Fortunately, when she went round to the house, Tom was outside in the garden, and she was able to tell him. Tom said that he would break the news to Dorothy later.'

'It sounds as if you feel responsible for her,' I submitted.

Dave laughed. 'Yes, in a way I do. I feel as though I've set her a bad example, as though I've let her down. And it's not just Dorothy; there's also Heather and Rachel and Ralph. I feel I've let them down as well.' He sat quietly for a few moments, considering his situation. 'I suppose I feel that I've been let down as well. I haven't been let down by the doctors and nurses, but I still feel that I've been let down.' Dave frowned. He looked perplexed. 'But having said that, I do feel more relaxed, more at peace.'

'You feel that you're gradually coming to terms with it?'

Dave nodded. 'Yeah,' he affirmed. 'Now I feel like I did when I was first diagnosed. I feel as though I'm able to cope. I know the future is uncertain, but I can cope with it. At the weekend, I felt afraid.'

'What were you frightened of?'

'You remember Lorraine?' Dave asked.

I nodded.

'Well, when I was first diagnosed,' Dave began, 'Lorraine was the first person who came in and spoke to me. Then she deteriorated and one night, there was this alarm buzzer at 3 am. It was a cardiac arrest call for her.' Dave paused as he endeavoured to express his emotions. 'At the weekend, I suddenly remembered that night, and I thought, "That's what will happen to me. Within the next 4 or 5 weeks, that's going to happen to me." I was frightened, and I hadn't been frightened before.'

'It is frightening when someone with the same illness as you dies,' I agreed.

'Yes, it is.' Dave shrugged his shoulders helplessly. 'Before I had leukaemia, I used to think of death, and it never frightened me. But at the weekend it did. But, having said that, it's more painful for the people who are left behind. They have to cope with the grief. I've always said to Paula that I don't want any emotional hymns sung at my funeral. I just want Bach's *Toccata and Fugue in D minor* played on the organ and then I want the hymn "Fight the Good Fight". I don't want any sad words. Well, I'm 47. I've had 47 good years.' He hesitated, collected himself and then said, 'But I'm not going to think about my funeral yet....' He gave me a defiant grin. 'At the weekend, I couldn't see my life more than 5 or 6 weeks ahead, but now I see it differently. I'm back where I was before and I'm convinced that the chemotherapy will be good and that I will get into remission again.' He paused and added, 'And even if I don't, I'll still fight. The thought of chemotherapy doesn't worry me. OK, I don't look forward to getting sore throats again, but I'm not worried. As long as I can see something at the end of it, I can cope.'

'As long as you have a goal to aim for,' I surmised.

Dave nodded and, by way of explanation, he said, 'Yesterday, Dr Wilson came in and said to Paula and me that if there was no hope, he would tell us to go away and have a good holiday. "But," he said, "there is a good chance of remission, and we'll go for it." I think the minute he said that, I thought, "OK, go ahead with it."'

* * *

Dave resumed chemotherapy. Sadly, as the weeks passed, his disease failed to respond to the treatment and his hopes for remission slowly dwindled. Significantly, Dave took no interest in his daily blood counts. Despite his adamant words, "I'll still fight!", it was clear that his heart was no longer in the battle.

At the beginning of October, Dave developed a respiratory infection which then progressed to septicaemia. His physical and mental condition deteriorated rapidly and he became dependent upon the staff and his family. Although Dave struggled to regain his independence, his former vitality and sparkle were no longer evident. He died on 22 October 1987.

Dave's funeral, held on 2 November 1987, was a moving occasion. Over 500 people packed the village church to listen to the haunting music of Bach's *Toccata and Fugue* and to sing the words of the hymn that had meant so much to Dave during his life:

> *Fight the good fight*
> *With all thy might,*
> *Christ is thy strength, and Christ thy right;*
> *Lay hold on life, and it shall be*
> *Thy joy and crown eternally.*
>
> *Run the straight race*
> *Through God's good grace,*
> *Lift up thine eyes, and seek His face;*
> *Life with its path before us lies,*
> *Christ is the way, and Christ the prize.*
>
> *Cast care aside,*
> *Lean on thy Guide:*
> *His boundless mercy will provide;*
> *Trust, and thy trusting soul shall prove*
> *Christ is its life, and Christ its love.*
>
> *Faint not nor fear,*
> *His arm is near,*
> *He changeth not, and thou art dear;*
> *Hear then and do, and thou shalt see*
> *That Christ is all in all to thee.*

Postscript

A year after Dave's death, I received a letter from Paula. In the letter, she wrote of her experiences during Dave's illness: her shock at his diagnosis, her hopes and fears during the treatment and the subsequent transplant. She described how Dave had often pulled her through periods of doubt and despair by virtue of his positive attitude. Even on the unit, when she was so apprehensive and edgy, he had been there to support her. When she developed an infection and was unable to visit him on the unit, Dave would stand at the

4. DAVE

window opening on to the courtyard, writing notes to her and smiling, always smiling.

Later in the letter, Paula told me of her return to work as a legal secretary and discussed the family happenings. Although her life was busy, she recounted her continuing struggle with sadness and grief. Paula concluded her letter:

> *I find that I miss him more now than at first. It is harder to cope without him. Forever seems a long time.*

* * * * *

5. *Alan*

ALAN WAS BORN IN 1963. HIS YOUNGER BROTHER, PAUL, WAS BORN 2 years later, in 1965. Alan was not a studious little boy. He did not thrive in an academic environment, and in 1979 he left school to begin work as a labourer with a small construction firm. 3 years later, his father, Derek, died. As the eldest son, Alan felt constrained to assume his father's position as head of the household, and he endeavoured to support his mother, Sylvia, financially and practically.

In the summer of 1985, Alan began to feel unwell. There was nothing specifically wrong with him; he just felt tired and run down and he developed an unusually large crop of mouth ulcers. When the mouth ulcers failed to heal, he made an appointment to see his doctor. The doctor took a series of blood tests and the next day, when the results were obtained, he referred Alan to the local hospital. From there, Alan was taken to the haematology unit at the general hospital and commenced on chemotherapy.

For 4 months, Alan endured intensive cytotoxic and antibiotic chemotherapy. Then, finally, after the seventh course of chemotherapy, he went into remission. Unfortunately, a few weeks later, he came out of remission and was recommenced on induction chemotherapy. Thankfully, his leukaemia went into remission for a second time in July and he was started on maintenance chemotherapy. In November, a bone marrow rescue was performed. The transplant went well and, after only 3½ weeks on the unit, Alan was discharged home.

During Alan's illness, a number of other young people were diagnosed as having leukaemia. With his bubbly, outgoing personality, Alan fitted in well and made many friends among the group. From a medical perspective, however, he was sometimes difficult to manage. A rebel at heart, he often chose to ignore the advice of medical and nursing personnel. If he did not agree with an aspect of care, he simply 'bent the rules' and 'did his own thing'. For instance, Alan was a 'party animal'. He enjoyed the company of his friends and liked to go out with them in the evening. While he was on treatment, the doctors advised him to avoid places where large numbers of people were gathered. Alan was unable to abide by this recommendation and when he was discharged home he continued to go to parties and to go out drinking with his friends.

Although Alan's carefree attitude and behaviour was infuriating at times, it was impossible for the staff to dislike him. The ever-present twinkle in his eyes and the grin on his face always drew a return smile. Moreover, his irrepressible, fun-loving nature more than offset the frustration that resulted from his lapses in compliance.

During my first few months on the unit, I met Alan several times on the ward and in the clinic. At these meetings, we always chatted informally. Alan did most of the talking. He talked rapidly and incessantly; like a horse-racing commentator, he fired out his ideas in quick succession. It was exhausting listening to him and it was almost impossible to follow his ever-changing flow of conversation.

Due to Alan's erratic and turbulent mode of discourse, I did not intend to include him in the project. However, he found out about my work, and one day he asked me if I wanted to do an interview with him. It was with a sense of misgiving that I agreed and reluctantly arranged a date for our conference.

3 June 1987

The outpatient clinic was surprisingly quiet when I arrived. There were only a handful of people in the strangely peaceful waiting-room. I spotted Alan as soon as I entered the clinic. He was sitting in a corner, near the 'blood room'. He was settled comfortably in a chair, his arms folded across his chest and his legs stretched out in front of him, so that his feet rested on a magazine table. He was seated in an ideal position. From his vantage point, he could see everything that was going on in the clinic. He could see patients arriving at the desk; he could watch the comings and goings in the blood room and he could observe the doctors' consulting rooms in the corridor off the clinic. Rather than disturb him, I went in search of a clinic nurse and an empty room.

The clinic nurse showed Alan and I into the vacant consulting room. The room was starkly furnished with a small porcelain sink, a large oak desk and an examination couch, covered with the customary sheet of green paper. Alan and I sat down, one on either side of the desk.

As I set up my tape-recorder, I studied Alan's appearance. He was dressed in a pair of denim jeans, a green T-shirt and a yellow baseball cap. In stature, he was a tall, loose-limbed young man. Painfully thin and totally bald, I was hardly surprised that he attracted stares of pity from passers-by wherever he went. I switched the tape-recorder on and we began to chat. I asked Alan to tell me about his diagnosis.

'When they said I 'ad leukaemia, I didn't know what it was,' Alan announced, "cos I'm not into things like that. I don't read the papers or anythin' so I didn't realise what it was.'

'Can you remember what your thoughts were at that time?' I prompted.

Alan grinned. 'All m' mates thought I 'ad AIDS. I did too. So when the doctor come up and told me, "You've got leukaemia," I said, "Doctor, thank God for that!" 'E thought I 'adn't took it in, 'cos I was laughin' and jokin' about it, like I am now. But that's 'ow I am. I'm that sort of person.' He paused momentarily and then went on, '2 months later, it 'ad sunk in. Well, after the first couple of treatments, I did think about it. I thought, "Why me? Why 'ave I got it? Why couldn't it 'ave been somebody else?" I got a bit depressed about it.'

'You got a bit depressed?' I repeated.

'Yeah!' Alan affirmed. 'Well, at first I thought it was excitin'. I was really lookin' forward to comin' into 'ospital. When they said, "You've got to come in for a few weeks," I thought, great! I'd never been in 'ospital before. Well, 'cept for when I was a kid and I 'ad m' tonsils out. Apart from that, I'd never been in 'ospital. I'd been real 'ealthy.'

'So this was a big change for you?' I suggested.

Alan nodded. 'Yeah! It was. It was like a new adventure for me. But then, after the first couple of times I was ill, I'd 'ad enough. After the first three treatments, I didn't want no more. It was awful. I 'ad to come in every day for m' treatment. I'd go 'ome, be sick, come back in again, get more treatment, go 'ome, be sick again.... I got really scared about it. I got to the stage where I said to the doctor, "I don't want no more." 'E said, "Well, you know, you've come to the end of the treatments. You've got into remission and so you've only got to 'ave treatment now and again." So I came back. Then, when I relapsed and the doctor said I 'ad to go back in again, I couldn't 'andle it. I'd 'ad enough. I went to London and drove around for a while. Then I come back in 'ere and started the treatment again.'

'Was there anything that helped you get through the treatments?'

'Yeah,' Alan affirmed. 'When I come in, I used to bring all m' music with me, 'cos music does me great. It gets me goin'. I'd psyche m'self up as well. I'd say to m'self, "I'm goin' to get better, better, better. I'm goin' to fight, fight, fight, fight." Then I'd put some music on, and I'd think, fight, fight, fight, fight. Then I'd think about m' car. I'd think about gettin' out, about goin' out with m' mates and enjoyin' m'self. I'd think about the past and that kept pushin' me. It kept pushin' m' mind. I didn't think about bein' sick and bein' bad. I just kept pushin' it....'

'And the treatments, what were they like?' I enquired.

'They was really severe,' Alan declared grimly. 'They made me really ill and sick and 'orrible, and me 'air fell out. There was one lot of treatment, a red injection...' He looked up at me expectantly.

'Adriamycin,' I suggested.

'That's it,' he confirmed. 'And the other one was in a pump.'

'Cytosine,' I said.

Alan nodded again. 'Well, the cytosine made me a bit drowsy and yuk, but the red injection made me really sick an' all. Then they put me on the AMSA. That was disgustin'.' He grimaced. 'I 'ad a little bag, every day for 5 days. I was sick every day, and then 3 days later, I usually went straight back in with a temperature....' He paused for a few moments and then added, 'The treatments make you sick and a bit yuk, but it's the bugs that you pick up after when your counts drop that worry people. The last spell I 'ad in 'ospital before the transplant was about 6 weeks long. They couldn't find out what was wrong with me. In the end, they just let me go 'ome with a temp. It went after a while. But when I was in 'ospital for 6–7 weeks at a time, it got me down, 'cos I was just laid in bed . Then when I went 'ome, I was as skinny as a rake and I 'ad to put all m' weight back on again. I 'ad to go out and build m'self back up so that I could go out with the boys.' Alan chuckled roguishly.

'It's a constant cycle, isn't it,' I rejoined. 'You come in for your treatment; you get an infection...'

'That's it!' Alan interjected. 'I'd lose all m' weight, and I'd lose all me 'air. M' body was changin' all the time. And I'd get these awful temperatures....'

After each course of chemotherapy, Alan invariably contracted an infection. On these occasions, his temperature soared and he was readmitted to hospital for antibiotic chemotherapy.

'You used to get very high temperatures, didn't you?' I reminded him.

'Yeah!' Alan agreed. 'The first temperature I 'ad, I thought I was dyin'. I thought I was goin' to overcook.' He chuckled. 'Well, I didn't know what 'ad 'it me. I'd never 'ad a temperature like that before. But after I'd 'ad three or four, I didn't worry about it no more. It was common, like, and I was expectin' it. If I 'ad a temperature of 40°, like, it didn't worry me. I just relaxed. No, I've got a good attitude towards it now and it doesn't bug me as much.'

'Did it bug you before?'

'Yeah, it used to,' Alan acknowledged. 'Well, I was always ill. I was always in 'ospital and it broke up all m' relationships. It tore me away from everyone.'

I paused and then asked, 'How did it do that?'

'Well, it tore me away from m' family and friends. I used to be really close to all m' mates and their girls. Then when I come in 'ere, I broke away from 'em, so they wasn't so close.'

'How did you do that?' I enquired.

'Well, I told 'em that I'd done things, which I 'adn't, just to break 'em away so they wasn't so close. I used to go out with m' best mate every night of the week. Now I see 'im once a week, maybe twice. But I 'ad to break away, 'cos it was better for them.'

'It sounds as though you feel responsible for them,' I suggested.

'Yeah, I do,' Alan conceded. 'It's the same with m' girlfriend. Before I come in 'ere, we were goin' strong, but that all went down'ill. I don't blame 'er. It's just that I was doin' m' treatment and I 'ad to shut 'er out. I didn't want to be close to 'er. Well, I didn't want to be close to anyone, not until after the next transplant. After that I'll be a bit better. I'll get me 'ealth back and I'll be able to sort somethin' out. But while I'm on treatment, I just 'ave a good time. And as far as relationships go or gettin' close to anyone, just forget it. I've got a wall round me. I go so far and then no more. No, I ain't got anybody close to me.' Alan slouched back in his chair, a downcast and sorrowful expression on his face.

'Hopefully, that will change,' I said encouragingly.

Alan glanced up and grinned. 'Yeah! When I'm better, I'll get back into it. I'll build m' friendships up again. But it's goin' to be 'ard, cos I'll always be thinkin', "Oh shit! I might be ill again." I'll always 'ave that thing at the back of m' mind.'

'How do you cope with that fear, Alan?' I asked.

Alan's grin broadened. 'I'm a bit wilder!'

'You're a bit wilder?' I repeated.

'Well, I don't care about other people. I just care about m'self and what I'm goin' through. I know everyone is worried about me, but if I let all them worries get on top of me, I'd 'ave a nervous breakdown, so I try and keep on top of it. I go out and live normally. I go out with the boys, drinkin' and 'avin' a good time.' Alan chuckled mischievously and admitted, 'I used to go out even when I was bad and on the treatments. The doctors told me not to, mind. I'm not supposed to go against their advice, but I 'ad to now and again....'

'It's a part of your survival mechanism, isn't it?' I suggested.

Alan nodded. 'Yeah! I like goin' out with the boys. Well, I'm an outgoin' person and, when I've got breaks in the treatment, I go out and enjoy m'self.'

'What does your mum say?' I asked wickedly.

Alan grinned. 'She just lets me go.'

'Really!' I exclaimed.

'Well,' Alan confessed, 'she nags me to stay in all the time, but I go out. She don't mind me goin' out; she's sort of open about it. M' mates 've 'elped as well. They're always ringin' me up and gettin' me out. They really tried 'ard to make me feel one of 'em....' He paused briefly and then, with a quick glance at me, he said, 'You know, it's 'ard not 'avin' any 'air. You stand out from everyone else. While I was on the chemo, one of m' mates 'ad all 'is 'air shaved off. 'E 'ad a really short crew-cut, just so I wasn't the only one with no 'air. The others 've 'elped as well. When I first lost me 'air, I 'ad a lot of trouble gettin' into discos and things like that. But m' mates used to go and talk to the bouncers and get me in....' He paused again. 'I can't stay at 'ome. I 'ave to go out. I'm 'yperactive. I'm always on the go, doin' m' car and goin' out. I mean, that pulls me through. Like, now, when I go 'ome, I'll get depressed if I don't keep on the go. If I don't do nothin' for two or three nights, I'll get fed up with m'self, and I'll get scared and start worryin' about it.'

I nodded and enquired, 'Did you find it helpful going back to work?'

'Yeah, brilliant.' Alan affirmed. 'At work, I don't 'ave time to think about what's wrong with me. I'm a normal person. It's not like I'm in 'ospital and I'm bad. When I go 'ome, I'm a normal person, like everyone else.'

'It sounds as though you have a Jekyll and Hyde personality,' I laughed.

'That's it,' Alan agreed fervently. 'When I'm in 'ospital, I'm a different person from what I am outside. When I'm in 'ospital, I'm bad; I'm ill. I'm just tryin' to get through. But when I'm outside, I think, "Well, shit! I don't want anybody feelin' sorry for me."' He chuckled, his eyes glowing with reminiscence. 'When I came out the first time, I told all m' mates to treat me like I was normal, like nothin' 'ad 'appened. You see, it's 'ard when you 'aven't got no 'air and you're a bit skinny. People stare at you.' He gave a sardonic laugh, 'I used to walk into a pub and everyone would turn round and look at me. I 'ated it.'

'What about your friends? Did they try to protect you?' I asked.

'Yeah, they did.' Alan acknowledged. 'They were really good. They used to go into pubs and tell people all these stories about me, and then take me in. It was okay at m' local though. Everybody there knew I was bad, and they didn't treat me any different, which was great because I didn't want any pity.' He paused and then added, 'But I think m' relatives are more worried about it than me, like m' mum and m' brother. They worry about the disease and what'll 'appen to me, whereas I just go out and 'ave a good time.' He grunted, 'M' mum's always thinkin' about me, about what I'm doin'. When I go out, she makes me ring and tell 'er where I am, just to keep 'er mind at rest. Then when I get 'ome, she wakes up and wants to know 'ow I am. It's depressin' them all worryin' about me.'

'Have you talked to them about it, told them what you feel?' I interjected.

'Yeah, I 'ave,' Alan replied. 'M' mum knows 'ow I feel. She thinks I've got a good attitude towards it. M' brother don't talk much; 'e just keeps it in.'

'He's younger than you, isn't he?'

'Yeah,' Alan confirmed.

'Do you get on well together?'

Alan smiled roguishly. 'Well, we're always arguin', but then all brothers and sisters argue. But when I was in 'ospital, I learnt to appreciate 'im a bit more. We got close, even though 'e's the type that keeps it all in.'

'And what about your mum?' I prompted.

'Mum knows me. She just lets me get on with it, like. She comes and visits me in 'ospital and she knows what I'm like when I'm bad. I don't like other people seein' me when I'm bad and bein' sick. Well, when I was ill at first, m' mates all visited me. They come down when I was really sick. I was watchin' their faces. It wasn't very nice for me bein' sick and them all watchin' me. So I told 'em to stay away. I said, "You can come and visit me when I'm better." So that's 'ow it is now.' He grinned and then added philosophically, 'But down in the unit, I could 've done with one or two of m' mates comin' in, like. 'Cos I got fed up with the same old faces. I know it was m' mum and m' brother; but I see 'em all the time. I think it would 've been good if they'd let one of m' mates come down, to give me a bit of a boost.'

I was reluctant to enter into a discussion on visitor selection for transplant, and so I asked Alan about his experiences during the transplant, starting with the bone marrow harvest.

'Oh, it was no bother. I asked people about it beforehand and they told me that I'd be knocked out and I'd 'ave big needles put in m' back.

Scary!' Alan grimaced. 'But it was like 'avin' a football injury. It was like an injury I'd got in a football game, where somebody 'ad kicked me in the back, and after about 2 or 3 days, it went away.' He paused, thought for a few moments and then said, 'The anaesthetic made me a bit drowsy, but it was nothin' to worry about.' He shrugged his shoulders, indifferently. 'It's nothin', 'avin' an 'arvest or goin' on the cell separator machine; it's just part of the treatment. I just accept it and let the doctors get on with it.'

'And how about the transplant itself,' I interposed, 'because you weren't in for very long, were you?'

Alan grinned, 'No, I was quick. I was only in for 3 weeks. No, 3½ weeks. The first week I was sick an' ill. The second week, I was pickin' up. The third week, I was comin' on, and the last 8 days, I was just waitin' for m' cells to pick up. I suppose the first 2 weeks were the 'ardest, but I sort of flew through mine.... I didn't mind it down there.' (Alan pointed at the floor in the general direction of the transplant unit.) 'OK, the food's 'orrible, because m' taste buds went, and I felt lousy for a few days because of the treatment. But actually,' he hesitated and glanced at me, 'actually, I thought the treatment was 'arsher on the ward than it was on the unit. I was more sick on the ward.'

'Did you have radiation beforehand?' I interjected.

'No, I didn't this time. But I'll 'ave it with the next one. But I enjoyed it down there. A lot of people say, "Oh my God, solitary confinement!" Well, that's true. You're in a little room on your own and you 'ave to stay there. But it didn't worry me. I'd got m' telly and video and m' radio and m' phone, and the nurses would come and talk to me.' He chuckled happily. 'I used to talk to 'em for hours on end down there. It kept me goin' I think if you get bored, that's when things start 'appenin' to you. You know, you stop fightin'. But everythin' was fine....'

'So you're not worried about the next one?' I asked.

'No, I don't mind,' he replied. 'In fact, a month after I got out after the last one, I went to see Dr Green and I asked 'im when I could start the next one? I think the longer I wait, the more wound up I get. I'd rather 'ave it done quick and get it out of the way, so I can build m' self up again.'

'What will you do from now until the transplant?'

Alan shook his head. 'Oh, nothin' much. I might go on 'oliday next week. But I won't plan anythin'. If m' mates phone up and say they want to go to Blackpool for 2 weeks, I'll say, "If I'm around, I'll go. If I'm not, tough!" No, I live day by day. I don't plan nothin'. After the next one, it'll be different. Once I've got over that, got all me 'air back, sorted m'self out a bit, I can look to the future, look at what I'm goin' to do. But for now, I'll just carry on as normal, like I've been doin' for the last few years.' Alan winked at me. 'Goin' out with the boys....' He paused briefly and then continued, 'It's funny. Since I've been ill, I'm livin' differently. I've got to know a completely different range of people.' He winked at me again. 'I've met a lot of nice women, a lot of nice nurses.'

Feeling a little embarrassed at the amorous undertones in Alan's conversation, I hastened to change the subject. 'So you've changed a lot over the last few years,' I exclaimed. 'You've learnt a lot.'

Alan nodded and became serious again. 'Yeah. You're right,' he agreed, 'I've learnt a lot. I've learnt a lot about leukaemia, a lot about 'ospitals. When I'm ill and bad, I don't want to bother; but once I come round, I really want to know.'

'So you ask a lot of questions?' I proposed.

'Yeah,' Alan nodded. 'I do. I want to know what's goin' on and what they're doin' to me and what they're puttin' into me. So I find out when the doctors are comin' round and then I ask 'em about what's goin' on. Some people don't want to know too much. Like, they don't want to read anythin' in case they find out too much. But I find out as much as I can. Then I work out 'ow bad I am. Like m' temperature and blood pressure, I know all of that now, and if I 'ave a temperature, I know where I am and I can relax then.'

'Do you find that you learn a lot from the other patients?' I enquired.

'Yeah,' Alan rejoined. 'Well, when I first come in, I didn't know nothin' about leukaemia. All the boys, all m' mates were tellin' me that it'd make me sterile. The doctors explain things, but I like to talk to the others to find out what they've done and what they've been through.' He paused momentarily and then added, 'It's funny really, other people vary from me in what they go through.'

'They have different treatments and you can't really compare yourself with them, can you?' I commented.

'That's it!' Alan concurred. 'There were four of us on the ward. We all 'ad the same thing. One died when I 'ad m' transplant. Another one went to London; that was Richard, and 'e won't go through another transplant because 'e 'ad such an 'ard time with the first....'

'And what about the other one?' I interjected.

'Oh, Ray. 'E died as well....' Alan fell silent.

As I sat contemplating the implications of Alan's words, the door opened and a clinic nurse entered the room. She informed Alan that he was next-in-line to see Dr Roberts. Our interview was over. Quickly, Alan stood up and followed the nurse out of the room. I was left to pack away my tape-recorder and mull over the interview.

As I fastened my bag, I tried to identify my thoughts and emotions pertaining to our time together. I realised that the meeting had left me feeling unsettled. Although my feelings could have been attributed to the speed of Alan's discourse, I believed that my uneasiness was a reflection of Alan's own frustration with illness. He gave the impression that he couldn't care about his illness. He was blasé about the seriousness of his condition and, in conversation, he implied that he didn't care about the physical, emotional and social hardships associated with the disease. However, I suspected that his flippancy was an act of denial. Rather than face up to his own discontent and pain, he pretended that all was well, that life went on as normal.

* * *

In July, Alan was admitted to the transplant unit for his second bone marrow rescue. On this occasion, his transplant did not go smoothly. In the days that followed the procedure, he developed haematuria. Amazingly, however, Alan recovered. Against all the odds, his bone marrow grafted and his counts rose, and he was discharged home.

During his convalescence, Alan attended the day unit on a bi-weekly basis for blood tests. He was given supportive transfusions of platelets and packed cells as needed. I arranged to meet with him in the day unit.

23 August 1987

Alan lay on the hospital bed, dressed in a pair of denim jeans and a purple T-shirt. He looked pale and tired. His blue baseball cap was on the bed beside him and a transfusion of packed cells was in progress.

I took a chair, pulled it up to the bedside and sat down.

Alan looked up and grinned as the chair legs scraped across the floor. "'Ow are you doin'?' he murmured quietly.

'Fine,' I answered, 'How about you?'

'OK, I suppose,' he said despondently.

Eager to hear about Alan's experience on the transplant unit, I asked him about the procedure. 'How was the transplant?'

'Oh, all right,' he replied unhelpfully.

'Tell me about it,' I said encouragingly.

'Well, when I come back from the radiation, I was sick for a week. I couldn't 'old nothin' down. I couldn't eat. All m' taste buds went. M' stomach 'urt as well, from the radiation....'

'What was that like?' I prompted.

'It was like 'avin' sunburn inside m' body instead of outside,' he explained.

'Sunburn on the outside,' I mused.

'Yeah, it weren't bad to start with. Then 'bout a week later, I got a sore bum. I 'ad abscesses and I used to sit on the toilet and go both ways. The pain was dreadful. I'd never experienced anythin' like it before. I used to sit and cry....' Alan closed his eyes and lay back on the pillow.

'And then what happened?' I persisted.

Alan opened his eyes and announced, 'Well, after a while, that eased off. But then I started bleedin' in the bladder, which was even worse.' He grimaced at the memory. 'I was on morphine tablets for the pain. It was bad. But after 8 days, it cleared up.'

'It was rough period for you, wasn't it?' I observed.

'Yeah, it was.' Alan acknowledged grimly. 'I wasn't ill. But the pain was bad. It just sort of drained me and got me down.'

'Were you aware of what was happening?' I asked.

Alan shook his head. 'No, not really. I didn't know I was bad. The doctors told me, "Oh, it's nothin' to worry about."' He laughed sardonically. 'It's only since I've come 'ome that I found out 'ow lucky I am to be alive. They told me that what I 'ad in the transplant unit should 've killed me. I'm only the second person to survive what I 'ad, bleedin' in the bladder. I 'ad no platelets or cells or anythin'. I 'ad nothin' to stop it. Yet the doctors kept tellin' me, "Oh, it's nothin' to worry about. It's only a little thing."' Alan grinned again. 'I only learnt 'ow serious it was afterwards. One of m' mates 'as a girlfriend who's a nurse, and she told me 'ow serious it was. I didn't realise. But when I found out, I felt really good. I felt that I'd achieved somethin'. I was surprised at m'self, 'cos I thought I'd 've felt frightened, but I wasn't. I was pleased with m'self. I'm just glad that I didn't know before, 'cos I'd only 've worried about it....' He chuckled reminiscently and added, 'It stopped bleedin' then, and m' white count started to come up, and I went 'ome.'

'I bet it felt good to go home,' I remarked.

Alan shook his head. 'No, I felt rough. Last time I come 'ome, I was on top of the world. But this time it was different. For the first week, I didn't feel m'self. I felt groggy and I needed buildin' up.'

'Are you feeling better now?'

'Yeah,' he responded uncertainly, 'I'm quite well now, 'cept today I'm tired 'cos I need blood, and m' mouth's a bit dry. I just think it's goin' to take me a couple of months to get back on top again....' He paused briefly and then murmured despondently, 'All the people who was in the transplant unit with me are back in. They're all bad, like. Jeff's bad. 'E 'asn't relapsed; 'e's just bad with this graft versus 'ost thing. It's a bit worryin'. I'm not a depressive person usually, but it's gettin' me down, so I might start goin' out a bit more.'

'Going out a bit,' I repeated.

'Yeah! Well, stayin' in gets me down. I 'aven't got nothin' to do and I start thinkin' about things.'

'What sort of things do you think about?' I ventured.

'Well, like death, like the leukaemia's goin' to come back straight away. I worry about it, so I try and keep m'self occupied.'

'What sort of things do you do?'

'Oh, I work on m' van. I clean it and polish it and I do the mechanics and stuff. When I'm not busy with that, I listen to music and watch videos and go down to the pub.' He glanced up at me and then confessed, 'I went down to the pub last night. I was all right. I drank orange juice and stuff. But the thing is, a couple of kids on our street 'ave got chickenpox. One of 'em is a young boy. 'E's about 9 or 10. M' mate and I were talkin' to 'im on Saturday, and then the next day, 'e comes up in all spots. I was really panickin' about it in case I got it.' He glanced up at me again. 'But otherwise, I'm keepin' all right.'

'You're keeping all right?' I repeated.

'Well, I'm 50% better than when I first come out; I'm not 100%, but I'm 50% better. I reckon that as soon as m' counts are sorted out properly, I'll be on m' feet again. You know, I'll be out on the town again....'

In an effort to explore Alan's experiences in the transplant unit a little more, I asked him to describe his recollections of the stay. 'Do you remember much about your stay on the unit?' I enquired.

'Yeah, yeah,' Alan responded unhelpfully.

'What about the time when you were poorly? Do you remember much about that time?' I asked.

'No, not really,' Alan began reticently. 'I sort of wiped it off m' memory.'

'Did you do that consciously?' I persisted.

'No,' he denied, 'I think most people just forget. When you're in there day after day after day, you don't remember it. I can remember goin' down there. I can remember 'avin' the pain in m' bum, and I can remember watchin' telly, sleepin', playin' music and eatin' and drinkin', but that's all I remember. I don't remember bein' sick and bein' ill and all the rest of it. I was so ill, I just didn't think about it. It didn't click into m' memory, like.'

'It's a blur, isn't it?'

'Yeah,' Alan agreed. 'Although I was there and I was bad and ill, I forgot about it when I come out.' He paused a few moments and then remarked, 'I think the radiation knocks you down. I found the room over at Broadheath really got me down.'

'Was that while you were having treatment or while you were on the ward?'

'While I was on the ward,' Alan acknowledged. 'It was boilin' 'ot and there was no one around. I 'ad no one to talk to and I was lonely. The treatment wasn't bad, but the ward, ugh!' Alan grimaced in an effort to convey his feelings.

'What was...' I began. But Alan, preoccupied with his own concerns, interrupted me and reintroduced the topic of chickenpox.

'I've just got to watch that I don't catch chickenpox. You come out in a rash and things don't you?' He turned and looked at me expectantly.

'Yes.' I nodded. 'You come out in a rash.'

'I've 'ad it before,' Alan went on disconsolately. 'But the doctors say that, when your bone marrow is knocked off, it knocks your immunity.'

I nodded in confirmation.

'Do they check for chickenpox?' Alan asked.

I shook my head. 'I don't know, Alan. You'd better wait until Dr Roberts comes back and you can ask him. He'll be able to answer your questions.'

Alan turned and looked away. He stared gloomily out of the window. ''E'll give me a tellin' off,' he concluded.

'No, he won't,' I encouraged, hoping that Alan would change the subject. But Alan was determined to find out all that he could about the disease. 'What is chickenpox, anyway?' he persisted.

'It's a viral infection,' I replied.

'A viral infection.' Alan raised his eyebrows in an expression of surprise. 'Got antibiotics for that, germ bombs?'

I shook my head. 'No. They can give you an immunoglobulin to try and prevent you from contracting the disease, but antibiotics don't help.'

'Do you get temperatures with it?'

'Yes, you do.'

'Ohh!' Alan wailed.

'Have a chat with Dr Roberts,' I repeated. 'I don't know enough about it and I don't want to give you the wrong information....' We sat in silence for a few moments and then I asked, 'What are your thoughts for the future?'

'I dunno,' he replied.

'Are you thinking of going back to work?'

'Yeah,' Alan's face brightened. 'It'll build me back up quicker.'

'It'll build you up physically?'

Alan nodded. 'Yeah, physically and mentally. When I'm workin' I'm not stuck in the 'ouse all the time, and m' mind's occupied. Then when I come 'ome, I 'aven't got much time to mope around 'cos I'm off doin' stuff. No. I'd like to go back to work. But I'll 'ave another couple of months off first.'

'What will you do? Will you go out with your friends?'

'Yeah, sometimes.... I went out with 'em last night, but I 'aven't been out with 'em much since I went 'ome.'

'Is there a reason for that?' I asked.

'Yeah, some nights I'm just tired,' Alan muttered in a dispirited tone. 'I just don't feel like seein' anyone.'

'What about the other patients you know? Do you see much of them?'

Alan shrugged his shoulders in a gesture of indifference. 'Yeah, I see Ian. We go out together, every week. 'E's doin' all right. And I see Rich. But I don't talk to the rest of 'em. Well, if I see 'em, I'll talk to 'em. If I see 'em, I'll say, "How are ya doin'?"' He glanced at me quickly. 'I don't ask 'em if they're bad or anythin'. Like, I met Ray's wife at a show before I went in for m' transplant. We 'ad a chat, but I didn't know what to say to 'er. So straight away I told 'er. I said, "I dunno what to say about Ray. I'm sorry, but I don't want to talk about it."' He hesitated and then declared grimly, 'I know what it's like when someone's died. M' dad died. 'E 'ad an 'eart attack on 'is way to work, and 'e crashed the car. I saw 'im in the car. It looked as though 'e was just knocked out, just sleepin'; but 'e was dead. I was shocked. I didn't know what 'ad 'appened. People kept comin' to the 'ouse and sayin' they were sorry an' all. It just cracked me up. It was awful. I went to work the next day, and all the guys were amazed.' He grinned sheepishly. 'They didn't know what to say to me. So I told 'em. I said, "Just say you're sorry and shut up!" I couldn't cope with all the pity....'

Alan sat quietly for a few moments staring at his transfusion line. Then, without altering his gaze, he announced in a strangely flat and subdued voice, 'It takes a lot out of you, the leukaemia and the treatments. Like this time, it's quietened me down. Last time, I was real chirpy. I'll be back chirpy in a couple of months' time; but at the moment, I'm quiet. There's nothin' in m' brain. It's just blank....' With those words, Alan closed his eyes and lay back on his pillows. Our conversation was obviously at an end.

* * *

I did not intend to complete a third interview with Alan. The first two interviews had left me feeling ill at ease and dissatisfied. My frustration was due partly to Alan's deepening depression and his inability to express himself clearly. I was also unhappy with my own abilities as an interviewer. In particular, I felt inadequate and ill-equipped to expose and explore his thoughts and feelings.

A fortnight later, however, I met Alan on the ward. He had been admitted for investigations. His blood counts were in disarray and he had been started on intravenous antibiotics and amphotericin. Although he was ill, Alan wanted to talk. That afternoon, I sat and chatted with him for over an hour. This time our discussion was different. At last, Alan was able to admit his struggle with the disease and, in particular, his battle with depression.

'I'm not surprised I got depressed. I think the sun's got a lot to do with it. I sailed through the first transplant. It was in the summer and, before I went in, I 'ad an 'oliday in Portugal. I was up from 7 in the mornin' till midnight. I never got tired and I put on a stone in 2 weeks. When I come back, I 'ad the 'ickman put in, and I went down to the unit. I sailed through the transplant, and I was out in 3½ weeks and back to work.'

I steered the conversation back to Alan's depression. 'And this time it was different?' I suggested.

'Yeah.' Alan nodded. 'This time it was different. I 'ad the transplant in the autumn and it was really dark. There was never any sun, and I was so low when I come out; I couldn't cope. Anyway, for the first 2 weeks, I did everythin' I was told. I didn't go out. I ate all the right things. I didn't drink, and yet I still ended up in 'ere. It was awful, and I was really depressed.'

'Tell me about that: what did you feel like?'

Alan shrugged his shoulders. 'Well, I didn't want to talk or do anythin'. I just stayed in bed and pulled the covers over me 'ead and slept all the time, like Ron does. I knew I was down, but I couldn't do anythin' about it at the time. I knew I just 'ad to get out.' He paused and then added as an afterthought, 'I'm on the up, now. I'm puttin' a bit of weight on, me 'air's growin' back, and I've started pullin' the girls again.' He grinned mischievously. 'I've fallen in love with one of the student nurses. I play pranks on 'er and things.'

'Alan did you ever feel suicidal?' I asked, directing the conversation back to Alan's depression.

'Yeah,' he admitted grimly.

'Tell me about it,' I prompted.

'Well, I understand now why people do it. 'Cos sometimes I felt like I wanted to go to the top of a tall buildin' where I could scream and shout and cry. When I felt like that, the only thing that really 'elped me was talkin'. I could unburden m'self.'

'Who did you talk to?' I enquired.

'Oh, m' girlfriend. Trouble is,' he murmured, 'when I was 'avin' treatment, she assumed that I didn't want to talk. She just didn't understand....'

'What about your mum? Could you talk to her?'

Alan shook his head. 'No, I couldn't talk to 'er either. No, if I need to talk to anyone, I 'ad to go round to one of m' mates. We'd 'ave a couple of cans and then we'd talk. I'd tell 'em everythin', 'cos I could do that when I was drunk....' Alan paused for a few moments and then commented philosophically, 'When I got really depressed, m' friends

5. ALAN

would come over and we'd 'ave a few beers and we'd talk. Then we'd go out on the booze and we'd get drunk.' Alan glanced at me and added, 'I could lay the fear when I got drunk. I could lay it when I went disco dancin' and drivin' as well. When I got really depressed and wound up, I'd go out in the car and drive really fast or I'd go to a disco and dance all night, till I was absolutely exhausted. That drained the build up....' He paused and nodded to himself. 'But talkin's the best thing. I like to talk, 'cos if I 'old it all in, it messes me up.'

'Have you always been able to talk?' I asked.

'Well, sort of,' Alan began. 'M' mates couldn't cope with it at first. They just thought I was goin' to die so they wouldn't talk to me. But they accept it now. Some of 'em still can't talk to me, though, but they do listen....'

One of the things that Alan needed to talk about was his fear of relapse. 'I was scared of relapse. The other three I was in with 'ave all died. They've all relapsed. When the third one died, I got to the point where I thought it would 'appen to me next. I used to panic every time I 'ad to phone in about m' counts. When I picked up the phone, me 'and used to shake, and every time I 'ad to come in, I'd spent hours on the loo. It was OK once I was in. I'd just get on with it. In fact, I was OK as soon as I'd gone upstairs and packed m' bag. But I kept gettin' these 'igh temperatures. And every time I got a temperature, I used to think, "It's the leukaemia." I'd feel awful until I was in 'ospital and the doctors come and told me that I'd got a bug and m' counts were okay; 'cos when anythin' goes wrong, I automatically think that the leukaemia's come back.'

'So you can never really forget about it, can you?' I observed.

Alan shook his head. 'No, I can't forget. It's always at the back of m' mind.'

'Do you try and block it out?' I asked.

'Yeah,' Alan confirmed.

'Are you successful?'

He nodded. 'Yeah, most of the time. It flicks back now and again; but most of the time, I can just forget it. But it's always there, like. It's always at the back of m' mind, the thought that it might come back, that I'd 'ave to go through it all again, all the treatments, bein' sick and ill all the time with 'igh temperatures. That thought's always there'

'What would you do if the leukaemia came back?' I interjected.

Alan hesitated briefly and then replied, 'I've seen a lot of people just give up when they 'eard the leukaemia 'ad come back. They couldn't 'andle it. They couldn't cope with the thought of goin' through all the treatment again.'

'And what about you?' I persisted.

'I've 'ad it if the leukaemia comes back,' he announced. 'Well, the other three all died, so I know I wouldn't make it. Well, look at Dave. 'E was so well, and 'e did everythin' 'e was told while 'e was in the unit. 'E ate everythin' 'e was given. 'E even 'ad pilchards on toast,' Alan chuckled, 'and 'e'd go on 'is exercise bike. I'd 'ear the chain clankin' round on it, 'cos 'e'd really go. 'E was the best person to be in with. 'E was so positive, and 'e was such an encouragement. I couldn't believe it when I 'eard about 'im.' Alan shook his head in disbelief. 'I'm just glad that I 'eard about 'im when I was on an up. And then with Emily and Jeff....' He grinned sheepishly at me. 'I don't want to die, but I'm not afraid of death. You know, the last transplant changed me. I'm much quieter now. I'm different. I don't drink now.'

'Did you used to drink a lot?' I asked.

'Yeah,' he affirmed. 'After m' first transplant, I used to get drunk all the time. Every weekend, from Friday evenin' to Sunday afternoon, I'd be stoned. It was the only way I could escape. Now, I can't do that. I can't get drunk, 'cos I know it doesn't do me any good.'

'It doesn't do you any good,' I echoed.

'No. You see, if I go drinkin' now, it takes me several days to recover, whereas before it would only take me a day. So I don't do it. I don't take dope either. Some mates offered it to me as a way of escape, but I said no.' Alan turned and looked at me. 'I didn't know what it would do to m' body, so I wouldn't take it....'

'Have you changed in any other ways?'

'Yeah.' Alan nodded. 'M' friends 'ave changed.'

'In what way?'

'Well,' he said, considering the question, 'like, I can never get close to anyone in 'ere. Not really close. I like mixin' with the others, like Ian. We get on real well. Trouble is, when I'm in 'ospital, I only see the ones that are ill.' Alan pointed towards the recumbent figure, lying in the bed adjacent to his own. 'See what I mean?'

I nodded my response.

'Most of m' friends 'ave gone now, as well. Well, 'cept Richard. I see 'im quite a bit.' He paused and chuckled. 'It's funny. I never thought 'e'd pull through. 'E didn't look the type who would fight. In fact, I didn't think, 'e 'ad any fight in 'im. When 'e come back from the intensive care unit, I was amazed. I never thought 'e'd make it. 'E looked so awful when 'e went down. Anyway, 'e went to London after that. I was really sad when 'e went, 'cos I'd lost one of m' mates. But 'e came back after 'e'd 'ad 'is transplant, and we talked.'

'What did you talk about?' I prompted.

'We talked about transplants. 'E told me not to go in for the mismatch, but to 'ave the double autologous.' Alan recollected. 'So we talked about the chemo and the different treatments I could 'ave....' He paused and then went on, 'Trouble is, they don't know 'ow good these autologous transplants are. Dr Green says a double autologous is as good as a donor, but they're so new that 'e doesn't really know. What do you think about it?' Alan turned and looked at me expectantly.

I shook my head. 'I don't know, Alan.'

Alan shrugged his shoulders, helplessly. 'No, the best I can 'ope for is to live until I'm 35. I don't expect to live beyond that, but you never know. They may find a cure for it in the next 2 years, and then I'll be OK.' He grinned happily at the prospect of a potential cure.

'What are your thoughts for the future?' I ventured.

'Oh, I don't think about the future. OK, I've planned an 'oliday in Spain, but that's all. I wouldn't plan anythin' important, like gettin' married. It's not fair to the girl.' He glanced quickly at me. 'If everythin' goes well, I might, next year. 'Cos if it's OK after a year, I should be all right. But I'll just 'ave to wait and see, won't I?'

Our conversation continued on into the afternoon, finally ending with the arrival of the supper trolley. I left Alan tucking into a plateful of chicken casserole, rice and mixed vegetables.

As I cycled home, I thought about Alan, his illness and his future. Although the outcome of his transplant remained uncertain, I felt that he would face the time ahead with a new confidence and maturity. The last few months of treatment had not been easy for him; however, his struggle with depression had enabled him to confront his disease. To a certain extent, he had at last managed to come to terms with himself and his leukaemia.

* * * * *

6. Jeremy

AT 50 YEARS OF AGE, JEREMY WAS A MAN OF MANY ROLES. AT 18, HE HAD left school and trained at agricultural college. He then spent several years working in Canada before he returned to the United Kingdom to take up a lecturing post in agriculture. 8 years later, he moved to South Wales with his wife Janet and their four children and settled into farming full time. In 1983, Jeremy began studying for an Open University arts degree. After completing the course, he embarked on a new career as a social worker for the blind. In his spare time, he continued to utilise his farming skills by running a small hobby farm, supporting livestock and a few acres of arable crops.

In June 1985, Jeremy underwent a routine medical check-up. The results of his blood test were abnormal and he was referred to a local hospital for follow up tests. Expecting the usual 3- or 4-month delay, he was somewhat surprised by his rapid admission to the hospital 2 days later. Here further tests were performed, and these led to the diagnosis of acute myeloid leukaemia. Jeremy was transferred to the regional haematology unit for treatment.

On admission to the unit, Jeremy's blood picture was poor, showing a 90% cell involvement. A regime of aggressive cytotoxic chemotherapy was started immediately. Jeremy explained the effects of his treatment.

'This meant that the treatment of chemotherapy I had affected practically all of the other organs, including the heart and the kidneys, and I got pneumonia and various other things. So for 2 months, I was very ill indeed, including a visit to the kidney dialysis unit.'

Over the next 12 months, Jeremy received eight courses of chemotherapy. He was hospitalised repeatedly due to episodes of recurrent infection and acute illness. A persistent temperature of 37–38°C left him feeling tired and lethargic. Time passed unnoticed. Unable to concentrate on reading or writing, his waking hours were filled with the distractions of radio and television programmes, the vital hours with Janet and the occasional visit of a friend who travelled up from home to see him.

Finally, in May 1986, after the seventh course of chemotherapy, Jeremy went into remission. He received a further course of consolidation chemotherapy, and in September 1986 he returned to work, resuming his social work commitments. At high risk of relapse, Jeremy accepted the opportunity of an autologous bone marrow transplant. The transplant date was set, and in January 1987 Jeremy was readmitted to Rhiannon for the routine medical tests prior to transplantation.

My first meeting with Jeremy occurred during this period. Knowing my interest in the leukaemic patients, the ward sister telephoned me one morning and advised me to come in to the hospital and visit Jeremy. I arranged to meet him later that day.

As I write, the memory of that meeting flashes into my mind. I can see Jeremy sitting cross-legged on his bed, dressed in a woollen sweater and a pair of grey corduroy trousers, diligently knitting. Concerned about wasting time, he was using this final hospital admission to make his own preparations for transplant. With tuition from Janet, he was busy learning to knit (he was hoping to make a transplant scarf); he was also teaching himself to read Braille.

We chatted for several hours that afternoon, discussing among other things Jeremy's life as a social worker, his family and his hopes for the future, his poetry and his forthcoming transplant. Towards the end of our meeting, I asked Jeremy if he would consider writing about his leukaemia experiences in a retrospective account of illness for me. He agreed and then, as an afterthought, he commented, 'I'll have plenty of opportunity to write over the next few weeks.' Additionally, he consented to meet me again following his transplant for a formal interview.

---

18 March 1987

It was a cold, wet, grey afternoon. Jeremy sat in the sister's office on Rhiannon Ward. His large, chunky, hand-knitted sweater was pulled up over his abdomen, allowing the intravenous tubing free access to the Port-A-Cath connection port in his chest. An infusion of platelets dripped periodically.

Jeremy was making a steady recovery from his autologous transplant. Slowly, his strength was returning. 4 weeks after his discharge

6. JEREMY

from the bone marrow transplant unit, he was driving himself to hospital from his farm in mid-Wales for the routine twice-weekly appointments. At these times, blood tests were performed and, if necessary, supportive infusions of blood products were administered.

Jeremy's body bore the tell-tale signs of illness. His face had a healthy, weatherbeaten appearance due to the side-effects of chemotherapy (and to the years of prolonged exposure to the elements) and his tall, gaunt frame had little muscle or body fat. Sensitive to the cold, Jeremy invariably wore several heavy, woollen sweaters and a thick, woollen hat in order to keep warm. Sitting relaxed in a low armchair, his long, bony legs stuck straight out in front of him. Jeremy talked, calmly and confidently.

Having completed the clinical details of his illness, Jeremy began to explore his own response to the leukaemia and its treatment. He described his growing awareness of illness. Apparently, he had been unaware of the seriousness of his situation initially. Too ill to even care, he played a passive, sleeping role. Gradually, however, he realised the true nature of his condition. He recognised the fact that he could die and he became anxious to fulfil his family responsibilities. Jeremy was always very good at budgeting and planning ahead. Since he and Janet had to bring up four children on an uncertain farming income, he had to be. He therefore had a comprehensive life insurance policy and kept careful monthly accounts. Nevertheless, following his diagnosis, he sought to ensure material and financial security for his family. As soon as his condition improved, he investigated the pension arrangements that went with his job, and he and Janet started a long-term savings scheme.

When talking about his illness, Jeremy rarely paid any attention to his own physical and mental suffering. Indeed in our conversations, he often underplayed the pain he had experienced. He was blasé and chose to brush aside my occasional comments of pity. In contrast, he acknowledged the many hardships that Janet had faced during his illness. As he explored her battle with leukaemia, his voice coloured with emotion.

'Janet's perhaps had the hardest time. I was a fairly passive member most of the time, but she was aware of the risks. In the early stages, she was far more aware than I was...although I didn't realise it at the time. I only knew how much time she spent with me, coming in every day to see me. But I didn't realise the spiritual strain, as it were.... It's interesting, she normally gets asthma and hay-fever, but while I was ill it never appeared at all; it completely disappeared, whereas now it's come back slightly. Physically, she kept very well, although the mental strain was quite considerable....'

At the time of Jeremy's illness, Janet was head teacher in a high school mathematics department. Jeremy believed that this job was her lifeline. It helped her to cope with the stresses and strains associated with illness. In the event of his death, he believed that the job would provide her with financial and emotional security. He, therefore, encouraged Janet to continue working throughout his illness. He said simply that, apart from the children, it was the most important thing in her life.

As Jeremy talked about Janet's situation, her response to his illness, I wondered how he had felt when he was first diagnosed. Did he feel frightened or angry when he heard the news of his illness?

'I should have been, but I wasn't. I don't know if anger came out in some other form. I don't think so. I think I was so philosophically interested in the leukaemia, in seeing if there was any reason why I got it or not, I was diverted.... Frightened? I didn't know what it was all about, and by the time I did know, I was too ill to feel frightened and things....'

'Do you feel frightened now?' I asked.

Jeremy paused briefly and then said, 'No. Apprehensive, yes. I suppose that if I was told that the leukaemia had come back and that I had to go back on chemotherapy and go through it all again, then yes, I might feel frightened. But I put that thought out of my mind. I know it's there and, if the subject comes up, I will discuss that I have a 50% chance of life or death quite happily with anybody. But I look at it in a fairly academic way. I'm not going to be frightened of something that won't happen....'

'How about the children? How have they coped?' I enquired.

'Well, we probably made it too common-or-garden for them, which I think was the right approach. In theory, they accepted my death. In practice, I don't think they would have done.'

Apparently, the four teenage children were kept fully informed of their father's illness and they were encouraged to ask questions and to express their thoughts and feelings. Jeremy's illness affected each of them differently. Angela, the oldest child, reacted strongly. Upset, unable to come to terms with her father's diagnosis, her life totally disrupted, she threatened to drop out of college and join what Jeremy called 'an extreme religious group'. With the help of the group's pastor, Jeremy and Janet intervened and the crisis was averted. Angela returned to her studies with a deepening and strengthening of her Christian faith. In contrast, the three other children, Stuart and the twins Gill and Emma, appeared to cope more easily. Indeed, they seemed to benefit from the illness experience.

Jeremy explained, 'They grew up, if not overnight, they grew up in one year at a normal development of 2 years, which I don't think did them much harm...and I think overall that the illness has brought us much closer together as a family.... But certainly, their support and encouragement was crucial for me, particularly Janet's.' Jeremy paused and sat in silence for a few moments. 'I'm not a great one for visitors.... Most people are very keen to have lots of visitors, and these visitors are the highspot of their day. I would say my visitor is the highspot of my day, and not my visitors. But having said that, as a patient, you really do need a lot of active support. To a large extent, I found that my active support was coming from outside the hospital, with people writing in with cards and sending good wishes, and lots of people praying for me. There was one Christian group, perhaps I could tell you something about that group because something very extraordinary happened to them....' Jeremy stopped and turned towards me, waiting for my response.

I nodded. 'Yes. Go on.'

'Well, the group is in Surrey, and the contact was through a friend whom I knew very well. The group had prayed and thought of me a lot, particularly one weekend when I was very ill indeed. It was a crisis weekend. Initially, the group tried to direct their thoughts through the person who knew me; however, this changed. Apparently, there was a German boy called Franz in the group, and when I later met the boy, he said, "How pleased I am to meet you because you've changed my life." I found this very hard to believe, but he explained, "Yes, perhaps not in big things, but in small things. When John [Jeremy's friend] came to talk to us about you, we saw a photograph of you and then we prayed for you. As we prayed, I felt a desire to go out to you.... Basically, I'm a very selfish person and this is the first absolutely unselfish thing I've ever done." When the group met later to pray for me, they prayed through this Franz, and since that time he has been a different person.... It's extraordinary, and I can't explain it, but I feel that I know him in spirit rather than know him in the flesh....'

The spiritual dimension of his life strengthened Jeremy's physical and emotional abilities to cope with illness. It also augmented his existing support network of hospital staff, family members and friends and promoted his subsequent healing and recovery. Jeremy recognised the importance of his spiritual life.

'I don't think I would have been alive without this spiritual dimension. I certainly wouldn't without the hospital, all the care and treatment I received, the extra attention that busy nurses haven't got time for and the occasional bullying, especially in support of the dietician's horrible brews....' Jeremy wrinkled his nose in mock disgust. 'But I think this sustaining of the spirit, the feeling that so many people are caring for you, does give an extra strength in the fight against disease.'

In light of his strong faith and his belief in the power of prayer, I was surprised when Jeremy then confessed his refusal to receive individual prayer. Earlier in his illness, during a period of convalescence, he had attended a 'healing service' at a local church. At the end of the service, members of the congregation were invited forward for prayer. Although friends and members of his family urged Jeremy to go forward, he would not go. Jeremy explained his decision to me.

'I think my healing was done over a much longer period and in a much quieter way through the hospital. The medicine was absolutely essential. It's just that you can make slightly better use of it through your mental approach. Although I don't really understand it, I've seen enough since I've been in hospital to realise that this mental spiritual side is very, very important.... Jonathan [the hospital curate and Jeremy's close friend], my second visitor in the transplant unit, pointed out to me the parable of the ten lepers. All the lepers were cured, but only one came back, and Christ said to him, "Rise and go; your faith has made you whole" [Luke 17: 19]. I've no doubt that the other lepers were cured, but they weren't very much better off, whereas this man was a whole human being again....'

We continued to discuss spiritual healing and the benefits of a positive mental approach. Unless he was acutely ill, Jeremy always tried to understand the therapeutic action of the drugs he was receiving. He then used relaxation and simple visualisation and meditation to augment their effect.

'I think you've got to remain positive all the time.... Once you start saying, "Oh I can't do this, this is awful," you've lost that much leeway already and you're going to be that much slower in the medical side curing you. I'm quite sure that if you can keep positive you're getting the most from the medical side....'

'In this respect, did you find it helped talking to other patients, those with a positive attitude?' I asked

'Only a few. It's partly because we're all at different stages, we're all well at different times. When I was feeling well, they weren't.... But there were one or two of the 20–30-year-olds who I did get quite friendly with and who I found quite helpful.... The older patients weren't any help. They seemed to be a little more accepting, a little more helpless. So I think the ones who were actually fighting it were a minority. It didn't come through at the time, but when I look back, it comes through fairly definitely.' Jeremy spoke slowly and thoughtfully, carefully considering each statement he made. 'It's the individual ones who are positive and optimistic. Overall, I didn't get much help.... But there was one man who came in and talked to me, and he was a great help. The sister arranged for him to come. At the time, I felt he was just thinking along the same lines as me. But now in going back, I think he did give me quite a lot, and I think to talk to the right person, the person who's thought his way through, is good.'

'What about you? Would you go back?'

'Yes. But it's only recently, since I've gone through the whole cycle and I've begun to put things together in my own mind that I feel able to talk to someone else. In the early stages, I'd got so much to take on board that I didn't have anything to give....'

'You had a lot to take in?' I repeated. 'It sounds as though you didn't know much about leukaemia before you were ill?'

Jeremy nodded. 'I didn't really know what leukaemia was, to be honest!' His face wrinkled into laughter. 'I was in blissful ignorance until after the crisis point had passed. Now you hear about leukaemia all the time and everybody knows about leukaemia. But in those days, no one knew about leukaemia. In fact I was able to write a poem to the effect that leukaemia was a disease that no-one had ever heard of. It's funny. I seldom ever change my poetry, but I had to change this bit as it stood up like a sore thumb. But no, I just didn't realise the implications of it, and I'm very pleased that I didn't! All the way through this, I've found that the hospital have told me just about what I needed to know. I needed to know what was going on. I didn't need to know how ill I was....'

He paused briefly and then went on, 'I must say, now I am better and have had the bone marrow rescue, I would like more knowledge, but the treatment is so new that nobody can quite say what the course is.... It's a bit frustrating because I don't know whether I'm keeping up to par or not. I find that if I do push myself too much, I immediately have a bad day, so that's enough signal at the moment to go a bit steady. I'm driving to hospital and back now and that's about the maximum I'll do. In general, I don't go out in the evening. I did go out and find a sheep yesterday. I don't think it did me any harm.' Jeremy paused and smiled quietly to himself. 'But I do want to go back to work now. I found it a very great therapy when I went back the last time and I would be shattered if anything happened to stop me going back this time.'

Now that he was 'well on the road to recovery', Jeremy was eager to resume his work commitments. In light of his desire to regain control and to reclaim his old life, I wondered how he had coped with the bone marrow transplant. Had his adjustment to patient life, a life of renewed dependency and passivity, been difficult or had he slotted back into the familiar role with relative ease?

'For 6 months there was uncertainty whether the counts would drop sufficiently for me to have the transplant. Consequently, when they did drop, it was the climax of my recovery. With leukaemia to start with you come in, there's not much you can do about it. You're a patient; you're getting all the medical care you can get. But once you're on the transplant side, you've made a voluntary decision to go in there. That's not an easy decision, particularly if it's a donor transplant, because it may be that you're not going to be well for up to 2 years afterwards, and that does need quite a lot of psychological preparation.'

Jeremy paused for a few moments before describing his own thoughts prior to transplant. 'When the door shut behind me for 6 or 7 weeks, I didn't know how I was going to cope.' Jeremy shifted his position in the chair. 'The treatment didn't worry me too much. I just didn't know how I was going to cope with being in a room by myself, where nobody could come in, just a nurse, and where my visitors had to be behind a glass screen. They had to have masks and gowns and all the rest of it.... It wasn't particularly easy, but it was nowhere as bad as I'd expected it to be.' He paused again, endeavouring to recapture his experience. 'A lot of the conditions were the same as the ward. But I did have the bonus of getting to know the nurses a lot better because they were having to come in and clean out my room, and I saw a lot more of them. Actually, I was surprised that it went as easily as it did.' He smiled and added, 'I was not surprised at being terrified when it first started! The medical preparation was fine, but it was very difficult for me to envisage what would happen to me. I had a list of 20 minor queries that soon fell into place when I arrived on the unit, but it was difficult knowing what to ask before I went in.'

Jeremy turned and stared out of the window. 'I think when you go in, you've got to be prepared for passive getting well. The high temperature, not feeling very well, sleeping a lot, but as soon as you begin to get better or you're able to read or able to do something else, it's important to have the proper facilities there to do it. I think if you're not prepared to do something active or have a hobby or whatever, then you're going to find that time drags very slowly.... I took about four different things in. I didn't think I'd be using them all, but in fact, I did, so I never found that time dragged particularly. Now in the general hospital, it's different. When I wasn't particularly ill on the ward, I found that time was liable to drag....'

Our conversation continued until Jeremy's transfusion of platelets was completed. Then, having said goodbye, I went out of the room, leaving Jeremy to have the Port-A-Cath needle removed and the intravenous infusion taken down.

* * *

Over the following 6 months, Jeremy and I met occasionally after one of his monthly outpatient appointments. As we chatted informally over lunch or an extended coffee break, I gradually came to know the person behind the disease. During our conversations, we explored many topics, including family issues, work experiences, farming, poetry, religion and Christian faith, and the concepts associated with illness and health. These discussions both clarified my own thoughts and beliefs and allowed me to share in Jeremy's struggles and frustrations.

Jeremy was not immune to the fears that accompany illness. He realised that there was no guarantee of a cure, and he knew that his leukaemia might relapse at any time. A seed of doubt lingered in his mind. Periodically, Jeremy became anxious and depressed. He worried about the future, his own suffering and the welfare of his family. Although these periods of anxiety often coincided with episodes of acute anaemia, a known cause of depression, Jeremy was saddened by his emotional instability. It revealed his inability to hold on to the promises of Christ in a time of need, and he believed that it indicated his own lack of faith and spiritual weakness. Recently, as he struggled to reconcile his emotions and his Christian beliefs, he had turned to his Bible for solace. In the book of Matthew, he found verses that were both meaningful to him and helped him to appraise his situation. Jeremy quoted the verses to me.

> *Come to me, all you who are weary and burdened, and I will give you rest. Take my yoke upon you and learn from me, for I am gentle and humble of heart, and you will find rest for your souls. For my yoke is easy and my burden is light. (Matt. 11:28–30)*

In October 1987, Jeremy returned to his job as a social worker, full time. Shortly after his return to work, I met him in the hospital canteen. We had coffee together and chatted. Jeremy talked about his slow adjustment to normal life. Initially, he had been frustrated when the doctors were unable to predict his rate of recovery. But gradually, by using his body as a monitor, he had learned to determine his daily routine. Essentially, he learnt to regulate his level of daily activity according to his physical wellbeing.

'You've got to work within your capabilities,' he informed me. 'Even if the work is piling up, you've got to take on what you can do and try and get on with it. But at the same time there is no point in stretching yourself so far that you're too far stretched, either to help other people or to be able to have those reserves yourself. Because I do realise that I often have to go to bed very early. I sometimes come in in the evening and that's that, I can't do any more, and I realise that I'm pushing myself as hard as I can and still being effective – my effective limit is now as high as I can put it....' Jeremy paused and then went on, 'I'm lucky actually, and I tell people this, I'm either ill or I'm well, there's precious little in it. I'm talking particularly again of the working situation: I'm either feeling I'm fully there or I'm beginning to feel a bit cold. I'm on flexitime, so if the signs are there, I'll finish work half an hour early, and it's usually a question of going to bed and resting part of the evening. But I'm fairly near the limit and I'm in the fortunate position that the limit is up there and it drops very fast so I'm not in the sort of grey lag area. I'm either going full pelt or I'm saying, "Right, stop!" I've had enough physical problems that when the signs say stop, I stop!'

They began to serve lunch in the cafeteria. Not wanting to get caught in the meal time rush, we decided to leave. Before we parted, Jeremy agreed to do a second taped interview with me. We arranged to meet following his next appointment at the hospital.

---

25 November 1987

The small consulting room was hot and airless. Noise from the busy haematology clinic was clearly audible. There was a buzz of conversation as patients and their relatives sat chatting in the corridor. They were all waiting, waiting for blood samples to be taken, waiting for blood test results to arrive and waiting eventually for a consultation with one of the doctors on duty. Jeremy and I sat facing each other across a large wooden table. A large, well-used, green blotting pad had been pushed to one side of the table top. Although a little pale, Jeremy looked fit and well. Since our last meeting, he had gained weight and his hair had grown. His hair was thick, dark and curly and had flecks of grey. I switched the tape-recorder on.

Jeremy flicked through a magazine, attempting to locate an article written by a fellow cancer sufferer. The pages rustled and flopped over noisily. He began to discuss the article, describing how the author discussed the various factors that are known to cause cancer. He used the article to examine his own thoughts about cancer.

'I won't say that it hurts, but it speaks to me.... It's not that I daren't go back. I'm not interested in going back to see why I got ill, whether there was a psychological thing back in childhood. There might have been, there might not.' Jeremy shrugged his shoulders to convey his lack of concern. 'To be absolutely honest, I don't really want to know. But perhaps I needed the illness. I'm prepared to look at it from that viewpoint, that's slightly different.'

'You needed it?' I commented.

'I needed it to make me stop, to make me reappraise myself. To make me ask myself, "What am I doing here? Am I running round after my own tail?" and that type of thing.... What's the first paragraph say here? Not an awful lot. But that question did hit me, "Why did I need the illness?" Not, "What do I consider from the past could have caused the illness?" I've had a brief look at that, and I'm not interested. But looking back at it from the spiritual side, I do wonder what I can learn from it....' Jeremy paused for a few moments and then went on to talk about his children and the questions they had asked during his illness. 'Basically, I think the kids believed that it had come from the devil in some way.... If they'd been pressed, they'd probably have thought that it was something that I had done or not done. But as I believe that Christ is a God of love, I don't think he gave me leukaemia.... It has brought changes, though.'

'Can you describe those changes? I prompted.

Jeremy hesitated before answering my question. 'I'm talking about work now. When I'm asked to see the husband whose wife has died 2 or 3 months earlier, I feel I am able to talk to him if he wants me to talk, or I'm quite prepared for him to talk to me.... I feel that I have got the experience now to know what he's talking about. I think it's the experience of sitting back and seeing other people who were worse than me, their suffering and their problems, and then relating them to my own. I've done a little bit of counselling and I want to do more. Illness hasn't given me a new ability, but it's definitely strengthened the old ability of that type and I feel more at home with other people and their problems. In counselling others, I can't say I'm doing better, I only hope I am....'

The changes in Jeremy's counselling technique were a direct result of his own personal growth. In the process of coming to terms with illness and death, he had confronted and worked through a diverse and turbulent range of emotions, and, ultimately, he had come to accept his own mortality.

'When I was first ill, back in August 1985, I wasn't ready for death. There were a lot of things that needed doing and there were a lot of loose ends. Now, I'm ready for it.... I've done everything I can for the family and for myself. So if it comes, I know the loose ends will be tied, as far as humanly possible. On the other hand, I consider myself as being here in 20–30 years time, and I will fight death like hell when it comes. But as far as getting everything organised, like personal relationships, the farm, financial and family affairs, I literally do it today. I particularly make a point of spending time with Janet.'

'What about Janet? How does she feel about your illness and possible death?' I enquired.

Jeremy hesitated before answering. 'Janet would be prepared for me to die now as well. I'm not saying that she would be pleased, mind!' He grinned with alacrity. 'And to be absolutely honest, I don't mind.... But I don't want you to get me wrong, because I'll fight death. I'll never give into it, not until the last minute comes. But when it comes, that's that!'

I smiled at Jeremy's adamant words, his determination and conviction. He spoke hurriedly and excitedly, his thoughts and views tumbling out in rapid succession. 'Death doesn't worry me, although I do worry about the pain. But that helps me with the old people I meet. In many ways, I think illness is like old age. It prepares you for death. I heard somebody explain old age on Sunday....' Jeremy hesitated, searching his memory for the speaker. He smiled as the memory flooded back. 'I was with Janet at a house meeting, and an old lady said, "I'm getting nearer, ready for heaven!" When you're young, you're not ready for heaven,' he explained. 'The gap is that big.' Jeremy stretched his arms out wide, like a fisherman, trying to demonstrate the size of his catch. Then he slowly brought his hands together again as he continued. 'But as you get older the gap gets smaller and smaller and you're more ready for it.'

'You're more ready for it?' I repeated.

Jeremy nodded. 'Yes', he affirmed. 'Death is the natural end to life. I think most old people are not afraid to die. In fact a lot of them would welcome it, especially the ones living alone, and that makes me more at ease with death.... But, I don't like physical pain. I can do without it, and I've been lucky so far.... No, I'm not frightened of death. I don't want it, mind you. I like life. It's lovely, and I really enjoy it! But actual dying, I've been close enough to it in the past to realise that it doesn't hold any terrors for me.... The pain that goes with it, well that's not that great....' Jeremy stopped and sat in silence, apparently lost in thought.

Endeavouring to bring him back into the conversation, I asked him. 'You feel that you have suffered pain?'

Jeremy nodded. 'Yes, but it's difficult to describe. As I told you before, for some people, not me, it's boredom or depression...and you forget physical pain. I did a short poem called "Pain" when I had a very active, nasty, oesophagus. It was swollen, and I couldn't even swallow saliva. I wrote most of the poem while I was actually ill, because I knew that when I looked back on it, I would have forgotten that side of it....'

Pain

Pain   *the sharp end of fear*
        more bitter than death
Pain   *the devil drives in nails*
        to kill the spirit under siege
Pain   *this cruel intrusion*
        love tones its agony.

'I did have various sorenesses, but I think I was lucky in not having as much pain as other people.... But the occasional times when I didn't feel in control was frightening. It wasn't black and white, but it went through a mixture of shades from the physical side of control to the spiritual side. During a bad bout of pneumonia, I was very short of breath and I had to be put on oxygen. I found that very distressing because I was losing control of my own bodily functions. I remember that more than the actual pain of the disease. The pain I was able to handle, but the lack of oxygen and the breathing...' Jeremy grimaced.

'It must have been terrifying,' I sympathised.

Jeremy nodded. 'Yes, looking back, I remember I was more frightened at that stage. I can remember saying to the nurse who was looking after me, "Turn the oxygen up! I want more oxygen!" And she said, "It's up as full as you can get it!" I found that very frightening. Eventually, Janet got me on to the breathing she did in childbirth, and when I could do that I could handle it again....'

There was a knock at the door, and a clinic nurse entered the room, carrying a pile of patient records. Surprised, bewildered and embarrassed at finding the room occupied, she apologised and retreated into the corridor. The door banged shut behind her. Jeremy turned to face me again.

'It's interesting. This book I told you about; it's called *Not Once but Twice*, and it's the story of Tim Dean, who was healed of Hodgkin's disease and leukaemia. It's written by a friend of his and, where he's writing about Tim's spiritual feelings, I feel it's absolutely right, but where he's talking about Tim's pain and the medical side of things, I don't. I can feel that it's written by a third person and not by Tim himself....'

'How do you mean?' I wondered aloud

'Well, when you get a very sore throat or a very sore behind, you can get terrific pain. There's no doubt about that. But I think that pain can often be felt more by, not an outsider, but by a concerned third person.... I identified with Tim on the spiritual side of things, though. He was an Arts student, and basically he was very down to earth and very practical. Picking up on the spiritual side of it, I was able to identify with him quite a lot....'

Apparently, as Jeremy read the account of Tim's illness, he was forced to confront his own thoughts and feelings regarding illness and death. Slowly, the book helped him to reconcile his own beliefs, enabling him to come to terms with his leukaemia. He spoke slowly, carefully choosing his words.

'When I started reading again, it was the first book I read. Where it helped me was about halfway through the book, where Tim had come to an acceptance of the disease and an acceptance of death... It was a great help for me to have this acceptance, because from that base, I could go on. OK, I might die, but I knew that I'd do everything I could against it, everything I could to keep on living.... It made me realise that I wanted to go ahead.... I never got to the stage where I was prepared to die. I don't want you to think that I did! But, talking about the heightened spiritual awareness, I can look back and be fairly amazed at what I recorded of a period of my life that I've never had before and that I've never had since. The experience has shaped my spiritual life. It's brought together all kinds of loose ends, and I've got a confidence about it now, within a very limited sphere, which I'm prepared to put forward.'

'Can you tell me a bit more about this heightened spiritual awareness?' I suggested.

Jeremy leaned back in his chair, considering the question. 'I think you do get a closer relationship when you're ill. Okay, you've got to ask for it; you've got to want it. I don't think it's got to be in Christian terms, but it's much more difficult if not.... But when you're at a low physical ebb, you're much more open, and I think this openness allows the spirit to come in. When I was ill, there was very much a closeness to the spirit which was very helpful to me....'

'You felt a closeness?' I reflected.

Jeremy nodded. 'Yes: because of my poetry, I'm in touch with my subconscious, and I can turn my conscious mind off, allowing my subconscious will to go its own way. I use it in prayer as well as in writing poetry, thinking and meditating. During the time of my illness, particularly the time I was in the bone marrow unit, I found that my ideas of the last 20 years or so were starting to come together and make sense. I'm not saying there were new ideas coming in, they just seemed new to me because they were old ideas that were able to come down and able to be worked out....'

Jeremy's philosophical 'working out' centred on his Christian beliefs and the influence of these beliefs on his life. Gradually, during his time on the transplant unit, he was able to develop his own Christian manifesto, involving the person of God, Christ the son of God, the work of the Holy Spirit and faith.

Jeremy explored his thoughts regarding the experience. 'All these things, all these little jigsaw pieces fell into place.... And so, rather than somebody else coming along and saying, "Well, in Matthew 6 it says so and so; you're a non-believer because you don't believe"...at last I'm able to argue my own philosophy. This type of thing is something that has worried me for years and now I've grown past it. I feel that I've been given this great gift of time, this great gift of learning....'

* * *

Following our final meeting, Jeremy and I began to correspond, infrequently. Jeremy used his letters to keep me up to date with his family news and his state of health. He also used the writing to work through and clarify his own thoughts and feelings. In one letter, he asserted that 'no thinking person could come through a serious illness without some sort of change...'. He then described the many changes that had occurred in his own life during the 3 years of illness. He described how his values had changed and how his priorities had hardened. In general, he had become more appreciative of the simple things of life.

> When I went home, I found things were much more vivid. I would stop to admire a sunset or a flower, or I would enjoy some quite simple drink or something to eat when my taste came back. I also found the pursuit of money a very boring activity!

In a recent letter, he explored the impact of illness upon his life. In essence, he examined the personal meaning of his leukaemia. He wrote:

> This letter is a voyage of discovery for me and as such has a potential excitement, which might or might not be realised. I do not know where to start. I am even tempted to end here, because nothing I say can ever be substantiated and may never have happened anyway....

Jeremy went on to outline his personal beliefs and his understanding of Christianity – an understanding which he acquired through the moulding of his illness experience. As a Christian, he lived in the present. His two guiding principles for life were firstly, to worship God and enjoy his love, and secondly, to love his neighbour. As he travelled the road to recovery, he continued to learn and grow. Illness was a short and intense period in his life, and he now had to move on.

> However nothing is static...and in things of the spirit we walk along a very long road, and I have hardly turned the first bend.

Postscript

Unfortunately, Jeremy's bone marrow rescue was not 100% successful. He died on 20 February 1990, following a haemorrhage from a stomach ulcer.

Typically, Jeremy managed to lead a virtually normal life for about

2 years following the transplant. Indeed, he continued working as a social worker until the first week of January 1990.

Jeremy's faith in Christ increased steadily up until his death. Similarly, he and Janet grew very close over the last years.

Janet still works as a teacher. As Jeremy predicted, her work and her children are now her lifeline.

*　*　*　*　*

121

7. Richard

RICHARD WAS BORN IN 1961 IN THE VILLAGE OF BRYNTERION, A FEW MILES outside Bridgeport. He was the eldest son of Gareth and Brenda Newman. Gareth was a financial consultant, specialising in the European markets. As he worked primarily on the continent, Richard and the other two children, Christopher and Bethan, saw little of their father during their childhood.

Richard looked back on his early years with mixed feelings. His home life was happy. He also enjoyed his initial schooling which took place within the peaceful and sheltered environment of a rural junior school. However, at 11 years of age, he transferred to the local comprehensive school. Here he was classified as 'a slow learner' and was placed in the remedial class. Richard hated it and, over the next 5 years, he struggled to prove his academic abilities to the 'somewhat sceptical teaching staff'. He learnt very little and with classmates 'destined to become society's future problem cases' he made few friends. Eventually, he became so disillusioned with school that he decided to educate himself at home. He implemented a disciplined programme of self-directed learning, and subsequently managed to leave school with six 'O' levels and two 'A' levels.

Richard applied to Nottingham University to study geography. He was accepted and 3 years later, he graduated with a 2.2 degree and a new self-image. His student days were happy and productive and, in retrospect, Richard recognised that his time in Nottingham had allowed him to 'develop from a studious introvert to an almost extrovert character'.

Following his graduation, Richard went through a period of real learning. Unable to find a job which utilised his geographical skills, he applied for a managerial position in banking. He was appointed as a bank clerk and began a managerial training scheme. The training allowed Richard to develop his management and communication skills. It also enabled him to develop as a person; it allowed him to recognise the weaknesses in his own character, his feelings of insecurity and his dependence on others, and equipped him to overcome these frailties.

Towards the end of his training, Richard was diagnosed as having leukaemia. Once again, he was placed in a position of weakness and uncertainty. Initially angry and confused, Richard soon recognised that illness was a time of further reappraisal and change. 2 months after his diagnosis, he wrote in his diary,

> *Oct 6th*   *There are times in one's life when events change one's personality or outlook. This is one of those events. I believe that the me who went into this is going to die to the me who is going to come out of it. I have to ensure that I have a better appreciation of life from now on. I must change my thoughts, my beliefs in life and religion. Maybe I should read the Bible....*

Richard was diagnosed as having acute myeloid leukaemia on 28 July 1985. He had little warning of the catastrophe that was going to engulf him. Feeling run down and suffering from frequent nose-bleeds and niggling pains in his back, he decided to go on a walking holiday in Scandinavia to 'pick [himself] up'. Midway through his holiday, he almost died. He was flown home to Essex and his diagnosis was confirmed. A few days later, he was transferred to South Wales for treatment. His management training was suspended and he returned home to live with his parents.

Following his transfer to Wales, Richard underwent a barrage of medical investigations. The initial blood tests and bone marrow biopsies indicated extensive disease involvement and aggressive chemotherapy was therefore commenced immediately. Unfortunately, Richard's condition was slow to respond and on the fourth course of chemotherapy, his regime was altered.

Richard's treatment continued for months, a seemingly endless cycle of cytotoxic chemotherapy, infection, hospitalisation and finally a period of convalescence at home, prior to the next course of treatment. Eventually, plans for a bone marrow transplant were initiated. Nevertheless, Richard felt as though his treatment was getting nowhere. He became increasingly depressed. Finally, after the sixth course of chemotherapy, Richard went into remission. Unhappily, the victory was short-lived and costly. A few days later, he developed a severe septicaemia and was admitted to the intensive therapy unit with septicaemic shock. Too ill to comprehend what was happening,

Richard had to depend on other people's reports to complete the daily entries in his diary.

Jan 22nd	*Disaster! Went in with septicaemia. P took me in. I collapsed in hospital. Falling pulse and very high temperature. I was extremely ill. My kidneys packed in so they took me to Intensive Care, put a catheter into my bladder and gave me oxygen all night. Two big drips put in, an arterial drip – they had to cut my jumper off. Mum stayed.*
Jan 24th	*Dad came back. My heart was having difficulty pumping blood. The doctors did a superb job looking after me, as did all the nursing staff. I wasn't aware of what was going on.*
Jan 27th	*P and M came regularly. Time didn't seem to exist. I couldn't tell the difference between dreams and reality.... I thought I was in Scotland being treated. What the hell was going on?*
Jan 31st	*Came out of ITU. Back up to Rhiannon. Weird experience altogether. I was too confused to know what happened on ITU. I didn't know what was real and what was dreams....*

The experience proved to be a turning point in Richard's attitude and approach to the illness. Realising the seriousness of his condition, he decided to seek a second opinion regarding his treatment. After two consultations, he transferred to a hospital in London for additional consolidation chemotherapy. Later he made inquiries regarding the possibility of an autologous transplant. His early hopes for a donor transplant were abandoned when none of his family members proved compatible and the search of the donor banks in Britain, America, France, Italy and Germany proved fruitless. After extensive investigation and careful analysis of the remaining treatments available, Richard decided to have a double autologous transplant. This was performed in October 1985.

The transfer to London was more difficult than Richard had anticipated. During the months of treatment, Rhiannon Ward had become his second home. The staff, patients and their relatives had become his family and friends. Consequently, when he left the ward, he felt disconnected and experienced a sense of loss. Then when he arrived in London, he had to adapt to a new hospital environment and fit into a new hospital family. He felt like an interloper, 'as though [he] was hanging on to someone else's family'. However, once the treatments were under way, his feelings of loss, separation and alienation were soon dispelled. He was unaware of his circumstances and his concerns of the past evaporated.

In retrospect, Richard was unable to remember the events of transplant. Although he could recite a complete list of the drugs he received, verbatim, he could not remember actual details of the transplant itself: the transplant experience was a blur.

Richard explained. 'Well you spend most of the time just doped up out of your eyeballs. It's extremely strong chemotherapy. The doctors say that they could cure the leukaemia with the drugs that they've got. The only trouble is 99% of the patients are likely to die from it!'

Richard remained in isolation for 50 days. Gradually, his bone marrow function returned, and he was able to go home. Unfortunately, a few weeks later, he developed a pyrexia of unknown origin. He was readmitted to hospital, and then, for the next 10 months, he underwent extensive investigation and treatment. Sadly, the medical intervention was unsuccessful, and eventually Richard was referred to a liver specialist. He was diagnosed as having a non-specific hepatitis and was commenced on non-steroidal drug therapy. Slowly, his symptoms began to subside.

In May 1987, Richard returned to Rhiannon for a friendly visit. The visit was not a success. Although Richard enjoyed seeing the staff again, he found the whole experience terrifying. As he talked to his friends and walked around the ward, memories that had lain dormant for almost 2 years were reawakened. Later, he confessed that he was glad to leave the ward.

My first meeting with Richard occurred after that fateful ward visit. At the suggestion of a colleague, I contacted Richard by phone. After describing the details of my research, I asked him if he would be prepared to do a taped interview with me. He agreed willingly.

---

24 June 1987

Richard's family lived in a large, detached stone house on the outskirts of the village. The long and narrow garden was filled with flowers, shrubs and bushes, and was overshadowed by four towering beech trees. The property was situated in a quiet cul-de-sac.

It was a warm, sunny afternoon and the air was thick with the scent of honeysuckle. As I walked up the path towards the house, I wondered what the afternoon meeting would disclose. Not having met Richard before, I was curious about what he would be like. What would he look like? Would he be talkative or would he be 'the silent type', making our conversation stilted and formal? With these thoughts in mind, I tentatively rang the door bell.

Richard opened the door to welcome me. He was a tall young man, clean-shaven with short, spiky, mouse-brown hair. His clothes, a thin cotton shirt, corduroy trousers and a pair of strap leather sandals, appeared to be several sizes too large for him, accentuating his skeletal 1.88 m frame. Smiling broadly, Richard showed me into the sitting-room. Situated at the front of the house, the room was furnished simply and comfortably. At the far end of the room, two chairs and a sofa were positioned around a gas fire. Either side of the fire stood two large bookshelves. There was a small television set on a lower shelf, while the remaining shelves were covered with an assortment of books, magazines and newspapers. A pair of heavy, floral curtains hung at the window. Having set up a table for the tape-recorder, Richard settled himself on the sofa. I pulled a chair up to the table and sat down. We started to chat.

Richard was obviously a thinker. Throughout our conversation, he spoke slowly and deliberately, carefully choosing his words. After hearing the detailed account of his illness, I asked Richard if he had known anything about leukaemia prior to his diagnosis?

'To be honest with you, I didn't understand what leukaemia was. I'd never heard of leukaemia. I didn't think I was going to die or anything; I was just confused.... But to start off with, I just accepted everything. It didn't really dawn on me until Christmas what was wrong with me.' He laughed. 'It's remarkable how easily you slip into a hospital routine, forget the other life you used to lead. So I had the chemotherapy and just got on with it, without asking too many questions.'

'You didn't ask questions?' I reflected.

Richard shook his head. 'No! I think it was the shock of being in a strange system, a strange environment. I automatically assumed that the doctors were going to save my life, and the thing with the medical profession the world over is that they continually use abbreviations and words you've never heard of. Now, I don't mind using abbreviations. I've picked up most of the medical language that the doctors use. But initially I didn't understand....' Richard paused as he tried to recollect the details of his hospital experiences that were buried deep in his memory. 'About Christmas-time, a lot of people on the ward started dying. They were people I'd been friendly with. I was the type of person who wanted to get to know everybody, find out about their illness and treatment and compare them with myself. Then all of a sudden, these people started dying, and what really shook me was that they were dying from exactly what I had. So I started asking questions, demanding a lot more information from the medical staff. I started asking questions like, "Why aren't I going into remission?" While I was in hospital, I kept a diary and I wrote down the names of everyone I talked to, what they'd said and what treatments I was having. I always had questions.' Richard smiled and added by way of explanation, 'Well, it was my life at stake! Some people don't want to know about their illness; they can't handle bad news. Others need to know everything, and they can handle bad news. In London, I was able to sit down and talk to the doctors on level terms, for the first time. They told me everything I needed to know, and they treated me as an individual, an intelligent individual who could understand what they were saying!'

I nodded. I was aware that many patients, like Richard, found the loss of autonomy associated with hospitalisation difficult to accept.

Richard continued, 'While I was having consolidation chemotherapy, I felt that there was nothing being done. I was just sitting around, waiting for the leukaemia to come back. I'd seen people in my position die, waiting to find out if they had a donor on the Anthony Nolan Panel, and I didn't want to be in the situation where the leukaemia was dictating my treatment. That's why I went for the second opinion on the chemotherapy. I mean, I was the one who was running the risk of dying from leukaemia, and I'd rather die from an overdose of chemotherapy, trying to fight for my life, than die quietly from leukaemia!'

'It sounds as though it was important for you to make decisions and say, "Okay, I'll move to London and have treatment there."'

127

'Yes, psychologically it was,' Richard affirmed, 'because I knew that if I got into the situation where the leukaemia was dictating things, I was losing control. I felt that by making these decisions to get the best possible treatment, I was still in control.'

Richard's fear of losing control developed as a result of several factors, including his poor response to chemotherapy, his experience of acute illness and the illness and death of his colleagues. In the months prior to his remission, his diary accounts reveal his deepening depression.

Oct 25th	*Marrow test. Leukaemia still there. Treatment changed to a new drug – pink to yellow in a bag of saline. This should take about 3 hours to drip through. I'm depressed that I'm not in remission yet, and I hope that this doesn't have any bearing on the future. The plan is to have either Bethan or Chris as donor. I'm beginning to think too negatively.*
Oct 28th	*Went in to start new treatment. It involves a 3–4-hour transfusion (side-effect of removing the stomach lining!)*
Night	*Dad took me into hospital at about 1.45 am. I felt awful. I couldn't sleep or breathe. Had a sleeping tablet and managed to sleep for a couple of hours.*
Nov 4th	*Stayed in hospital for 15 days. High temp., i.v. antibiotics.... Midway through my stay, I got pretty depressed, started feeling sorry for myself and weeping needlessly. It's pointless to worry about events in the future that haven't happened. It gets me nowhere fast, like living for today as I plan tomorrow. I have to devote all my energy into living for today.*
Dec 21st	*Started to get depressed again. I've just finished a week's course of chemotherapy, half-strength. I can't describe how awful it felt. Is the cure as bad as the disease? Even if I do survive this, I'm going to find it hard to live in a world of death and destruction. I could die if this doesn't work! Was Auschwitz as bad as this? Probably, poor sods!'*

Richard wanted to be strong and to have total control of his illness. Realising that negative thoughts were detrimental to his health, he sought to identify and eliminate them. Instead of asking the question,

"Why me?" or blaming God for afflicting him with leukaemia, he looked for ways in which he could have contributed to the development of his disease. Although fully cognisant of the many physical and environmental factors that were known contributors to the development of leukaemia, such as viral infection and exposure to radiation or toxic chemicals, he was intrigued by the psychological origins of illness. He began a thorough self-analysis, searching for problem areas in his own personality.

> *April 11th* *Looking for psychological causes of illness. I always wanted to impress people, be liked by them. I worry about what others think of me. I've never felt really close to any one; I'm immune to other people's problems – this may have helped in causing [the leukaemia] by reducing the effectiveness of my immune defence system. I have devoted too much of my energy into defending my ego.*

In a further attempt to gain control over his illness, Richard sought to harness his emotions and feelings and to channel the energy this released into fighting his disease. Through reading and talking to other patients in the hospital, he was introduced to the Bristol Self Help Centre. The centre's main aim was to strengthen patients physically and psychologically, enabling them to overcome disease and infirmity. Richard visited the centre on several occasions. Impressed by their innovative methods and their interest in people, he studied and then adopted some of their techniques. My curiosity aroused, I questioned Richard about the centre and their activities.

'What did you like about the centre?' I asked

'There's a nice atmosphere about the place. It's a nice building and for some reason, it's always sunny and warm. After being there, I always feel a lot better.... The people there are really good, too. In hospital, I never see the people who are getting well, just the ones who come back, who've relapsed, and the new people coming in with leukaemia or another cancer. In hospital, they aren't willing to talk either, whereas in Bristol they do and they all want to fight and take control. Some of them have even stopped conventional therapy.'

'How do you feel about that?' I interjected

Richard's face took on a serious expression and he said, 'Stupid!

Brave but stupid! OK, there's casual evidence of people who've stopped therapy, and said, "Right, I have not got cancer." Lo and behold, 5 months later when they're persuaded to go for a check-up, the cancer has gone. But they're in the minority. The thing is, we're not all able to draw upon the strength that we have, so I think it's best to go for a multiple approach. Adopt the techniques that they suggest in conjunction *with* conventional treatment.'

Richard spoke from experience. As his illness progressed and he endured the rigours of chemotherapy, he adopted self-help, holistic techniques. He believed that these enabled him to rid himself of the destructive forces of stress and discord that accumulated during his treatment, allowing him to realise an inner peace. This peace and inner harmony in turn promoted his physical healing and personal growth. I asked Richard to describe the strategies he used. 'Did you use the mediation and relaxation with your treatment?' I prompted.

'Not at first,' he replied. Then he paused and asked me, 'Have you heard of the Simonton Institute?'

I nodded. 'Yes!'

'Well, they found that people who saw their illness as something that was strong did less well than people who saw their illness as weak. It's really important to imagine illness as weak.... Last week I was reading a book; it was the *Which! Guide to Cancers*.' He laughed. 'It had this horrible, daunting crab thing on the cover and every time I looked at it, it made me think, "Good God! How am I ever going to beat this illness?" So I changed it. I took a pen and made it look stupid, really weak and insipid. Then I said to myself, "Crikey, I'm bloomin' six foot two. I'm a big lad! It's not going to get me!"'

Seeking to explore these ideas further, I asked, 'So what do you imagine your leukaemia as?'

'Well,' he began, 'I'm a really fanatical war-gamer, so I used to imagine a load of knights, like the knights in King Arthur's Round Table.... I have a picture. It's of knights in shining armour, charging through an apple orchard with blossom everywhere. I imagine the knights coming down from the castle, charging through the orchard and going to beat the hell out of Mordred! I've got a good imagination and so, when I get fed up with that, I imagine the Star Ship *Enterprise*. The Star Ship *Enterprise* never gets defeated.... I think of the *Enterprise* shooting down enemy Klingons.'

'So the Klingons are like circulating leukaemia cells?' I suggested.

'That's right, and they're getting destroyed.'

As Richard recalled the strategy, he became increasingly animated. His face glowed as he waved his arms around, pretending to destroy the enemy battleships. We laughed together, enjoying an imaginary victory over the alien Klingons.

Meditation and relaxation were Richard's primary interests at the Bristol centre. However, when he visited the centre, he also took the opportunity of seeing one of the counsellors.

'All the counsellors have had cancer so they can understand all the conflicting thoughts and feelings you have and they can help you talk them out and find a positive way forward.' He glanced at me quickly and said, 'I found the counsellors were really useful. They had other things too, like vitamin therapy and special vegetarian diets.' He smirked. 'They weren't useful! With chemotherapy, you need a diet, yes, but it should literally consist of Mars bars and *lots* of calories!'

Silently, I laughed at the irony of Richard's words. Looking at his thin body, I couldn't imagine him eating a high-calorie diet, particularly not a diet supplemented with Mars bars.

Richard paused for a few moments before resuming his discourse. 'But the counselling was good. I think counselling is essential for people like me, and it would be really helpful if some of the nurses on the wards were trained in counselling. If they could help patients talk through their illness, it would help to relieve the stress.'

During his time in hospital, Richard had little opportunity to share his thoughts and feelings with professional staff; invariably, the staff were too busy to talk. Moreover, as his family were overwhelmed with their own pain resulting from the disease, he was unable to confide in them. Like many of his colleagues, he struggled through illness alone, isolated by his fears. Luckily, he was able to communicate with certain friends and acquaintances.

> <u>May 22nd</u>   *Had an enlightening chat with the Church of Wales priest. It was the first time I've had a real talk with anyone about spiritual matters. It made me feel much better. It felt good to be able to explain my feelings to a person who was not emotionally attached to me. I wouldn't upset him as I would my parents.*
>
> <u>June 1st</u>   *Had a really good chat with Brad. Being critically ill is lonely. There are only a few people that can reach you…. When you're very ill, there's a death sentence hanging over you. That's lonely! It's like being on one side of the street with everybody else on the other side. Only a few people cross the street to walk with you….*

Fortunately, his uncle did cross the street to walk with him. Richard explained how the relationship with his uncle developed. 'There was only my uncle who I could talk to. He had TB when he was about 19. Apparently, they used to lock away anybody who had TB or who developed spots, so he was in a sanatorium for 3 years. He was 22 when he came out. He used to tell me stories of how he had his lungs collapsed and then reinflated again…. But I can equate with him. The experiences that he went through were similar to the ones that I have gone through. While I was in hospital, he used to write to me every week. If I'd told him that something was upsetting me, he would write back and say, "Yes, OK, but you've got to look at it this way." He'd point me in the right direction and help me to sort things out.'

'So he was a correspondence counsellor,' I observed.

'Yes,' Richard affirmed, 'he was playing the role of counsellor….'

As Richard travelled through illness with his uncle, the two men drew together; their relationship deepened. Accordingly, I wondered if he had become closer to members of his immediate family.

'What about your relationships with your family? Have those relationships changed?'

Richard hesitated and then said, 'I suppose by the time I became ill, the family had grown up and had gone its separate ways. Only Bethan was at home with Mum. So in some ways, it did bring the whole family back together again…. I established a more personal relationship with my parents, particularly Mum. I also got really close to my uncle and aunt, who treated me like a son, and to some friends who used to give me lifts in and out of hospital. But I found that I was able to relate more to Bethan than Chris. It was surprising really, because I'm 10 years older than Bethan, whereas I'm only 2 years older than Chris. But I found Chris was difficult to get on with, 'cos his attitude was to treat me as if there was nothing wrong with me.... Eventually, I had to challenge him because there obviously was something wrong with me, and the moments when I broke through the barrier were extremely emotional. They were very painful for him. He couldn't deal with the leukaemia, because secretly he knew what was going on.'

'Secretly?' I reflected.

'Well, we just didn't talk about the illness or emotional things. He was away in college at the time, whereas Bethan was here. She used to go to the hospital with Mum and so she knew that there was something seriously wrong with me.... She worried about me, and she used to ask Mum what was happening. She was far more in tune with me than Chris....' Richard smiled as though he was enjoying some secret memory of his sister.

'What about your father?'

Richard's grin widened. 'He does all my fighting for me. When I don't get the information I want, I go to my father and complain and complain and send him off into battle.... Even when I went to London, I left him to do all the screaming and shouting. As a patient, I was too exhausted from all the treatment. I hadn't got the energy to complain. I had to have somebody like him to do all the fighting for me.'

> *May 18th*   Home feeling depressed. Asked Dad to start moving mountains! I feel really angry. I hate this illness. I'm putting a lot of pressure on Dad.
>
> *May 26th*   Dad spent last week raising merry hell with the medical establishment. He is working himself to the bone. Avenues are opening up that I never knew existed. Although they're long shots, they're filling me with hope.

As Richard talked about his experiences, describing the development of his personality and understanding, and the changes within his relationships, I began to realise the enormous impression that leukaemia had had on his life. I recognised too that over time his recollection of the emotional trauma of the early months had become clouded. The clinical details of illness were stored in his memory, totally intact. In contrast, his mind had 'blocked out all the unhappy things that had happened to [him]'. Consequently, it was only later when I read his diary that I gained a true impression of his experiences. As I read through the daily entries, I gained an insight into the fears that had dominated his thoughts. I learnt of his fascination with death, a fascination that flourished amidst the sickness and death of his contemporaries.

> Mar 31st *Pretty good week. I'm starting to put weight back on.... I can't help feeling that this is the calm before the storm. When the leukaemia comes back, it will be for good!! I dwell a great deal on the possibility of death, what it's like and what comes after it. I need a closer relationship with God in order to enjoy living. I need faith.... I keep thinking that I am going to die.... I know this is wrong, and I really want to live, but I get the feeling that parts of my body are already dead.... I appear full of life on the outside, but really I'm dead, and I'm waiting for death to release me.*
>
> Death *I fantasise about my death, e.g. what other people would say about me when I'm dead and they're standing around my grave. Sometimes I think that Mum and Dad don't really know how ill I am. I want to die to prove to them that I've got a killer disease. I want to die, because secretly I can't handle the pressure.*

As illness progressed, Richard recognised his preoccupation with death and his separation from the normal world. In order to combat the isolation caused by illness, he tried to go out and visit people when he was home. Unfortunately, his fear of infection constrained him. Then, during the times of hospitalisation, he lived within the reality of suffering and death. Each day, he grappled with thoughts of death and dying. Sadly, the familiar ward routine left him bored and uninspired, unable to resist the fear evoked by the merest sight or sound of the word 'leukaemia'.

Apr 24th	*Went into hospital today for a blood test and a bone marrow. All the old faces were in.... David bones hurting, Alec relapsed, Dale very ill, Jeremy poor heart condition and Ian stomach ulcers.... It's depressing, and it makes me want to give up hope.*
May 12th	*Monday morning. I'm feeling ill and I don't want to go in. I'm scared of catching a superbug.... Treated with dobutamine, Haemaccel and antibiotics. Dad stayed in with me.*
May 15th	*Dale died today. Will I be next?*
May 19th	*Bloody depressed again. Put on antibiotics. I hate Rhiannon, the environment, the sense of hopelessness of the patients, the inevitability of it all. I must fight it. God isn't going to take me....*

Despite the nightmarish quality of Richard's daily life, time passed quickly.

'I was in a state of shock, really; it went so fast. It lasted about a year, and all the time it was bang! bang! bang! There was always something happening. I knew what was over the horizon.... I tried to have a regime I could stick to, but I lost track of time while I was lying in bed. The days seemed to be weeks and the weeks seemed to be months. Now looking back, I can remember every course of chemotherapy, every illness, every bad time, but overall it seems such a short period of time. It's amazing. I really lived at 100 miles an hour!'

The concept of collapsing time intrigued me. I began to explore the concept with Richard. As we talked, Richard described how his perception of time, noise and speed had altered as a result of illness.

'I never found that things looked a lot brighter or became more precious. It makes me crack up when people say they look at flowers and...' He grimaced. 'But what I did notice was the speed of things outside hospital and the noise. Now, when I go out with my friends, they seem to talk so fast and they laugh so much. Everything is fast and loud; I get exhausted. I'm used to taking things slowly and not rushing around....'

'You've slowed down,' I remarked.

Richard nodded. 'Yes, after my op, the nurses used to allow me out for walks along the Tottenham Court Road. I used to be terrified, the sheer number of people and the traffic shooting up and down. I was dizzy.... Even now, I still haven't got completely used to it, so I go out into the countryside a lot more and have long drives around the lanes and things like that....'

'You spend a lot of time on your own?' I asked.

Richard nodded. 'Well it's 2 years now, and for most of that time, I've either been at home with Mum or with one other patient in hospital. I've got used to my own company.... Now I sometimes get annoyed when somebody starts intruding on it...,' he smiled, perhaps realising the irony of his situation, '...but the experiences and emotions that normally build up over a lifetime are really consolidated into a 2-year period. I've gone through everything, death, pain, tragedy, love, fear, joy, all in such an intense period. It's like surviving a great war that comes once a lifetime. Even if you die, you still get your fill of experiences and often more.' He paused again, searching for the right words. 'In many ways, it was a healthy experience. Nowadays lots of people just exist. All their experiences are crammed into their youth and they can't really remember the rest of their lives because they've done nothing that stands out.'

'And you feel...' I started.

Richard interrupted me and resumed his explanation. 'After this experience, I feel that life is precious. The blinds have been taken off my eyes and I can see how rich life is. I can see what a gift life is. This has taught me to live for today and not for the future, making plans I'll never complete. If I want to do something, I tend to do it now. I don't delay things.... Another thing, I find that life is a lot fuller now. Rather than rushing through everything, I take my time, and I appreciate things a lot more. For example, life in a big city, like London. OK, the people there might be earning hundreds or thousands of pounds a minute but when they retire, when they sit back and look at their lives, I'm sure that they're going to feel very dissatisfied....' Richard leaned back into the sofa.

'Do you feel sorry for them?' I asked.

'No! I should, but...if I hadn't had leukaemia, I'd have been just like them. I'd have stayed a trainee bank manager. I was aggressive in my career and wanted to do well. That was the meaning to my life. I wanted to say to my friends, "Look I'm a manager. I'm earning so-much. Look how well I'm doing!" But I knew I wasn't fully satisfied. I'd have become manager of a larger branch and then a larger branch. Then when I retired, I'd have realised my mistake. Now I know I can get a lot more out of life. The only trouble is, I'm not too sure how to go about it. And I think a lot of people who've gone through serious illness are the same. They're not quite sure what to do next. Should they go back into the routine again or should they find something more meaningful? While I was having treatment, it suddenly struck me that it would be hard going back to my old life.'

> *Apr 12th*   *Even if I survive, I'm going to find living difficult...leaving behind a lot of people who never returned.... If I survive, I know God has given me life for a reason. He wants me to do his work. I can't go back to the job–house syndrome. That sort of life is plastic and hollow. When I'm in here the outside world looks pretty unreal. The people aren't really alive. I sometimes feel that the only human beings are the ones who are suffering.*

I tried to summarise Richard's thoughts. 'So your old life has been lost because you realise that it was unfulfilling and now you're searching for what to do and where to go?'

Richard nodded. 'This is why counselling is important for people who've survived illness, to give them direction so that they don't lose the experience completely....'

I pursued the topic further. 'What about you? What are your thoughts for the future?'

'Oh, I've had lots of thoughts, but I'm not too sure of the direction I should go in.' He laughed. 'I've even thought of going in for nursing! But seriously, I would like to go into counselling, particularly coun-selling people who are seriously ill with cancer or leukaemia.... Maybe I can make a contribution, help them in some way. Perhaps I'm naive? I don't know, but before I do anything, I'd like to answer all my questions.'

'What sort of questions do you have?' I enquired.

He hesitated and then said, 'I want to know how to live a satisfying, fulfilling life and how to avoid getting stuck in the old grindstone, wheels going round and round.... When I was ill, I used to live one day at a time. Now I can look forward to a future. I've got plans. I know what I'd like to do, but it's so difficult to come to a decision, to go back into society....'

We talked on into the afternoon. When we finished, Richard drove me to the station in his mother's Peugeot. The roads were narrow and winding, bordered on either side by rusty wire fences and roughly hewn stone walls. Confidently, Richard swung the car around each bend. He was a good driver and the journey was exciting.

My train ride home allowed me time to collect my thoughts. A similar age to Richard, I understood many of the issues he struggled with. However, there were many things that I was unable to comprehend. His passage through illness had equipped him with a superior understanding to my own. In theory, I knew the need for meaning in life. Contrastingly, Richard *felt* the need and yearned for a sense of purpose in his new identity.

* * *

Over the following months, we maintained contact with each other by phone and by letter. Surprisingly, Richard's health refused to improve. His stubborn, flu-like symptoms became worse, not better and, although further clinical tests were performed, no firm diagnosis was made. We arranged to meet again in November.

---

17 November 1987

It was a cold but bright afternoon in late autumn. The sky was cloudless and deep blue in colour. Richard met me at the station and drove me to his home. As the car nosed its way through the traffic in the busy shopping centre, Richard brought me up to date with his family news. Apparently, his brother had spent a long weekend in Texas, visiting his girlfriend. With raised eyebrows, Richard commented on how Chris had only been able to afford a 4-day break, due to his hectic lifestyle. In comparison, Richard found that time hung heavily on his hands.

The house was quiet when we arrived. Only Bethan was home, and she was upstairs in her room, revising for her forthcoming 'O' level examinations. We went through to the kitchen, where Richard made a pot of tea. Armed with the tea-tray, we went through to the front room. As at the previous meeting, I set up the tape-recorder on a small round table and then pulled up an armchair and sat down. Richard sat on the sofa. He was relaxed and peaceful as he quietly sipped his tea. Despite having a full head of hair, his face appeared even thinner than before. His clothes, a thick woollen sweater and a pair of corduroy trousers, appeared to belong to someone much larger. I realised that he'd lost more weight since the summer. Later in our conversation, Richard confided that he liked to dress smartly, for he regarded this as a symbol of inner discipline. As he described his current physical illness and his inability to pursue and attain his goals, I realised how his present appearance must undermine his already poor self-esteem. As his attempts to control and overcome his new illness failed repeatedly, his morale evaporated. Richard spoke about his infirmity.

'At one stage, I was so bad that I asked to be admitted to hospital, which for anybody who's had leukaemia is pretty drastic! But the last 3 months, health-wise, I've just collapsed. When I saw you in the summer, I was feeling well. Now I sometimes feel worse than when I had leukaemia.' His voice sounded flat and disconsolate. 'With this postviral syndrome, I just feel below average the whole time. There's no feeling good, feeling great. It's frustrating! I'm still full of ideas, but if this syndrome continues I'm wondering how I can support myself in the future.... I'm 26 now and, although I'm grateful for my parents' support, I want to be out making a life for myself.' Richard paused and glanced up at the window before continuing, 'With the leukaemia, I could accept being at home. It left me free to fight. But now I'm well on top of the leukaemia, it would be a damn good thing if I could get out and start living my life again.' He smiled ruefully. 'About a month ago, I went away for a weekend and tried to look after myself. I was grateful for the end of the weekend....'

He paused for a long time, staring gloomily into his half-empty teacup. He looked forlorn and desolate. 'At first, I thought it was psychological. I thought that I'd become too dependent on my parents. But after being reassured by Professor Brown at the liver unit in London that I was suffering from definite physical symptoms, my muscles are wasting away. I know it's not my imagination.'

'Did you feel that it was your imagination?'

He nodded. 'While I was having treatment, I always used to bounce back in between the courses of chemotherapy. As my counts came back, I'd be feeling good. There's a mountain up here called Brown Ridge. It's 900 feet high, and I used to test myself by climbing it. Now I couldn't even climb the first 100 feet! It's ironic. When I looked ill with no hair, I felt good. Now my hair's grown back; I look well, and I feel awful!' He grunted. 'Sometimes I feel like shaving my hair off or something; then people would know I was ill.... On my third visit to the liver unit, I took Dad along, just so that he could hear what the consultant was saying.'

'You took him along. It sounds as though he needed to be convinced that you were ill,' I remarked.

'Well, for a while, people were wondering if I was putting it on. Basically, I look well, so I did have to prove to him that there was something wrong. Mum knew definitely, 'cos throwing your guts up every night isn't normal!'

In many ways, the new diagnostic label was helpful to Richard. It gave him a sense of credibility and identity. Having recovered from the bone marrow transplant, everyone anticipated that he would find a job and begin supporting himself. His recent diagnosis had removed that unspoken pressure. Now that he was definitely ill, family members and friends did not expect him to do anything. However, Richard knew that he had to support himself eventually. Otherwise, he had no future.

'Except the time I had septicaemia, I always thought that I'd beaten the leukaemia. I'd convinced myself that if I got through that, I could get through leukaemia. I thought I was indestructible. This has brought me down to earth again....'

'It brought you back down?'

He nodded. 'Yes. I was foolhardy enough to think that I could go through eight courses of chemotherapy, a transplant and emerge the other side without having anything wrong with me!' He laughed, sardonically and then began to explore his circumstances. Unsure of himself and the future, he was confused and bewildered. 'But I'm beginning to wonder if I can ever support myself. Illness changed me. As I told you before, my life was always a rush. I had to keep up with my friends. I had to get a mortgage before they did, all those stupid things.... Now those things don't matter any more; nevertheless, I don't want to be dependent on the State all the time. I suppose I look at my college friends. They're always talking about how much they're earning, and if they're not on £10 000 by now, something is seriously wrong!' He laughed, wearily.

'How do you find that pressure?' I asked.

Richard thought for a few moments. Endeavouring to express his feelings, he began to describe his relationship with a friend. 'I had one particular friend, a chap called Michael. We used to compete against each other in school and at university. He always tried hard to get a good job, and talked about how much he'd be earning in the future.... I was always one step ahead of him. But since I've been ill, he's really come on. It annoyed me at first. Well, whenever he saw me, he would tell me how well he was doing, how well his job was going and how much he was earning! Recently, he bought a new car, and now he's planning to buy a CD player....' He laughed. 'I was getting really envious, but, eventually, I just stopped and thought about it. I realised that he's always going to be short of cash, either a mortgage or a car loan. I realised that he'll never know real happiness because he'll always be struggling for the next consumer item.' Richard paused again. 'To be honest, it kind of bothers me, but it doesn't. I see life; I compare Michael's life and mine in terms of 10 years time, and I can't really see that he's going to be any better off than me. OK, he might have ten times more than me, but he's going to have ten times more debt as well. It's a vicious circle, struggling to have the things you can't afford.'

I wondered if Richard's feelings really matched his adamant words. He had lost many things through illness. His physical health, his career and his prospects for the future had all gone. He had also lost many of his friends. Now that he looked well, some friends had begun to contact him again. In this regard, he again talked about Michael, his friend and sparring partner.

'It was about a year into the leukaemia and virtually all communication had stopped. He'd gone from a life-long friend to a total stranger....'

'What did you do?'

Richard grinned roguishly. 'I went to see him and I gave him a really good stripping down. I enjoyed the argument because it was really annoying me that he wasn't bothering to see me or even write to me. Then I realised that it was a weakness in his character, an inability to cope. It's OK now I'm better, now I've got a head of hair and look OK. It's as though I've been on a long holiday. It's the same with the others; they all talk to me as if it hasn't happened.'

I tried to draw Richard out a little. 'Can you give me an example?'

He snorted with laughter and said, 'Well, a few weeks ago one of my friends asked me if I wanted a game of squash. I couldn't believe it. I could hardly pick up a squash racquet, let alone hit a ball!'

'So do you find that your friendships are changing?' I asked.

'Yes...' His voice lacked conviction. There seemed to be an element of uncertainty in his mind. 'I still hold on to the old friends, but I don't make a great effort to stay in contact with them if they aren't interested in me.' He shrugged his shoulders. 'The difficulty now is making new friends. Like last week, I went to the pub with some friends. Part way through the evening, I started to chat to a chap at the next table. After a few minutes, he asked me, "Oh, what do you do?" And I said, "Well, actually, I haven't been doing much for the last 2 years." He said, "Oh, that's all right. I know all about unemployment." Richard gave another sardonic laugh.

'What did you say?' I prompted.

'I told him. I said, "I've got leukaemia."'

'What was his response?'

Richard assumed an expression of mock astonishment. He put his hands on his knees, lifted his eyebrows and opened his eyes and mouth very wide. 'Dead! I think he was a bit worried in case I gave it to him or something.'

'Was that a typical encounter?' I encouraged.

Richard paused. 'I can't really say, because I haven't gone out of my way to make friends, mainly because I think, "Oh, here we go. I've got to go through all the old business." It's just a story; I've caught a big fish, and I've got to tell it over and over again. I get fed up with it. I don't want to go through the explanation again, 'cos I know what the reaction is going to be. But really, I must make the effort to meet healthy people, go back to a normal life.' He laughed again. 'It's like being a member of a really elite club – only it's not the sort of club you'd want to join!'

Back from her shopping trip, Richard's mum brought us another tray of tea and biscuits. We sat in silence, drinking tea and munching chocolate biscuits. As our conversation resumed, I asked Richard if he still thought a lot about his leukaemia.

'I feel fine now, with regard to the blood, so I don't think about it as a result of that. And as time goes on, it gets more and more difficult to think that it would come back. Looking back, it's as though it hasn't happened.... While I was in hospital, I was just hanging on, determined to survive. The centre of my life was just surviving, getting through all the treatment, the chemo, more chemo, the hospital, doctors, nurses, drip stands, whatever.... Now that's all gone, I'm almost floundering. It's difficult.' Richard stopped and gave a deep sigh. 'When I was having treatment, things were happening. Although I was in situ and it seemed like ages before something was done, in terms of emotions, it was like spending a couple of weeks at the front-line trenches. I was living off my nerves. Now all of a sudden, I'm in the back trenches, and I don't even know that there's a war on!'

'It sounds as though you're feeling a bit lost?' I commented.

'Yes! It's gone quiet all of a sudden....' Richard's voice sounded flat and dispirited again.

I hesitated and then, having gathered my courage, I asked, 'Do you ever feel suicidal?'

Richard nodded. 'I would be if I wasn't afraid of dying. I could never conceive of throwing myself off a bridge. It would hurt too much.' He laughed. 'It would be worse than the headaches. Really, that's one of the reasons why I never attempted suicide, even with leukaemia.'

'Did you ever consider it?'

He nodded. 'Only when there was a lot of pain.... But I should think that any healthy person would do. Actually thinking about it and doing it are two completely different topics. I mean, it's the fear of what would happen afterwards that prevented me from doing it. That fear kept me going through the leukaemia as well.... The fear of what's going to happen to me if I die. I suppose I've always recognised that there were religious threads in my life. But like most people, I didn't pay much attention to them.'

'Did that change?'

'Yes,' he affirmed.

'When was that?' I enquired.

'It was when I was in intensive care,' he informed me. 'I suddenly thought, "Bloomin' heck! This is it! I really might die." After that, I thought a lot about the issues of life and death, the meaning of life, number 42 or whatever. I tried to search for answers because I couldn't live my life thinking that when I died that was the end. I couldn't exist without believing that there was more to life....'

> _Mar 25th_   This illness brings you closer to God, only serious illness does. I have aged 50 years. I now feel as somebody of 75 would, wondering: what comes after death? What is the meaning of life? Does God exist? I am asking these questions because of what I am facing.

Frightened by the thought that he might die, Richard sought to rebuild a religious framework into his life. He returned to his Catholic traditions and started to go to church and take communion. He also started to read his Bible. Nevertheless, his questions remained largely unanswered. He became angry at the injustice of his illness and began to doubt the existence of God. He became depressed. Later, a chance meeting with an Indian priest enabled Richard to clarify and redirect his thoughts. The conversation encouraged him and gave him hope.

> _June 17th_   It's a tremendous experience having leukaemia. I can learn so much about myself, life, the universe. I can begin to make a journey into my spiritual self. My physical being can meet my spiritual being.

Unfortunately, Richard remained dissatisfied with religious beliefs that he considered simplistic and unrealistic. Even so, he still clung to his religious practices. He confessed, 'I still go to church and take communion because I enjoy the symbolism of it all. But I'm not convinced in the Holy Trinity. I believe in Jesus Christ. Historically, there was a man called Jesus who was a great philosopher. His theories, like "Love your neighbour and love your enemy", are great. But whether he was human or the son of God, I don't know!' He laughed and added, 'And if anyone does know, I wish they'd come and tell me, because when it comes down to it, that's why I'm scared of dying....'

'Has illness affected your ideas on...'

Before I could finish my question, Richard interrupted me. 'Well, yes. I think it's healthy to realise that you live your life within a framework of life and death. If you don't realise that you're going to die, you can't really live your life properly. In the West, we've lost contact with that fact, but in that respect, the leukaemia helped me. With leukaemia, death became inevitable.... And one day, I know the leukaemia will get me!'

'You believe that it will?'

Richard nodded, gravely. 'Yes. Well, leukaemia is death. I'm not referring to the illness, but I do realise that I won't live forever. And to live a fulfilling life, I have to live it for a reason. I can't just exist in a hedonist type of way, doing as I please. There are probably valid things I can contribute to society, no matter how big or small, even if it's just being nice to the guy next door....'

I attempted to summarise Richard's thoughts and reflect them back to him. 'So you realise that you lifespan is limited, and that you need to use your life wisely, you're responsible to others. Do you feel that illness has altered your ideas about God?'

Richard thought for a moment and replied, 'It made me think about God again. I've always recognised a spiritual thread to my life, but I've never bothered to investigate it. Now I think about it; I debate it with myself and, in that way, I ask questions. Like with Jesus, if I decide that he wasn't the son of God, that doesn't mean I don't believe in God. But I've got to look at it in terms of a God of the universe, an omniscient being.'

Richard sounded uncertain and perplexed. I wondered if he considered his current spiritual dilemma to be a form of suffering. In an effort to examine the concept, I asked Richard to define suffering in terms of his leukaemia. After some deliberation he said, 'There's been physical pain, and there's been a lot of mental suffering, self-doubt, questions that I can't answer and which nobody can answer for me. Eventually, the physical pain goes and I can forget about it; but the questions about faith and religion, the nagging doubts about whether the leukaemia will relapse, they never go away....'

'Those doubts are still there?' I observed.

'Yes! Like tonight, I'll probably have to take a few sleeping tablets, because I'll be thinking about everything I've been saying today. Pointless really, completely pointless. But my mind will be thinking about it.' He sighed. 'It's a suffering that takes a lot longer to go away.'

'Are you frightened by the possibility of relapse?'

He nodded. 'Yes, I am! If, for example, I brush my teeth particularly hard one day and I bleed, I automatically think, "Crikey, my platelets have collapsed!" Last year there was one occasion when I had a platelet reading and it was 71. Normally, my platelet reading is 271.' He smiled as he explained. 'The machine had got clogged up. Anyway I rang the hospital to find out what the count was, and they said, "It's 71." I panicked. I thought, "What, my platelets have gone!"'

'Do you still worry about your blood test results?' I interjected.

He nodded, sheepishly. 'I'm always thinking, "Is it a good 'un or a bad 'un?" With the weight of good ones, it would really come as a shock to have a bad one.... But when I get the envelope, I sit there for a while. Everybody else just goes "Crruchh!" (Richard made a noise like tearing paper and pretended to rip open an imaginary envelope) and walks off with theirs, while I'm sat reading mine! Initially, it's just a blur of figures.... But my last one was good and each time I panic a bit less.' Smiling, he added, 'Now when I go to hospital, I forget about the leukaemia. I just want them to find out why I'm feeling so bad! But...' He shrugged his shoulders. 'At least it takes my mind off the leukaemia, and I've been told that it has a positive effect on it. They say that the viral infection will help the body to destroy any remaining leukaemia cells.' He glanced at me. 'But it's strange. The leukaemia's been with me for so long now that I can't imagine any other sort of life. Sometimes I still wake up in a cold sweat, thinking that it has come back, and that I've got to go through it all again....'

'What would you do if the leukaemia did come back? Would you have more treatment?'

Richard furrowed his brow in concentration. 'At the moment, I don't know. I suppose in many ways it would be a relief not to have the chemotherapy. Dying would be a merciful release, rather than going through it all again. I wouldn't be scared of dying; I'd just be disappointed, disappointed that I wasn't going to have a longer life....'

* * *

Following our second meeting, Richard continued his battle with ill-health. The symptoms that appeared after his transplant grew steadily worse and, in a taped message dated 3 March 1988, he complained, 'I now feel worse than when I had leukaemia.' Apparently, a combination of severe headaches, diarrhoea, nausea and vomiting left him feeling tired and listless, unable to concentrate and depressed. He often cried to alleviate the tension he felt. Beset by the nagging fear that his illness was 'all in his mind', Richard sought psychiatric help. A psychologist in London reassured him that his symptoms had a 'definite organic cause', and, subsequently, three separate diagnoses were confirmed: postviral syndrome, candidiasis of the stomach and non-descriptive hepatitis.

Having survived the battle with leukaemia, Richard found it difficult to generate and maintain the motivation necessary to oppose these new illnesses. Goal-setting was his only means of creating the incentive he needed to fight.

In May 1988, I received another letter from Richard. In the letter, he described how he had recently received two separate invitations to appear on national radio and regional television. Seemingly, he had been asked to participate in programmes devoted to leukaemia and bone marrow transplantation. One was a panel discussion and the other was a documentary.

Although Richard was thrilled by these invitations to appear on radio and television, he was frustrated by the restrictions and limitations that resulted from his own physical disability on a day-to-day basis. The lessons he had learnt from leukaemia, 'to take risks' and 'to live life to the full' were rendered futile by his lingering malaise. He felt disconnected and trapped inside his body. Despite his previous determination to survive and function as a separate entity, his prospects for the future remained uncertain. Unable to work, he endeavoured to use his spare time creatively. Sometimes he would borrow his mother's car and explore the local countryside around his home, discovering a deserted village or the ruins of old castles. At other times, he would simply sit and read as he endeavoured to answer the many questions that remained in his mind.

The final words of Richard's letter captured his feelings of disillusion:

> *I know I'm unique, and I feel especially different as a result of my experiences with leukaemia and this new illness. I appreciate life more and when I'm fit and able, I now know how to live. It's just frustrating at the moment....*

* * * * *

8. Bill

BILL EVANS WAS BORN IN THE MIDLANDS IN 1933. HE CAME FROM A LARGE family and had five brothers and two sisters. Bill's early childhood coincided with the years of the Depression. During those years, his father was unemployed and money was scarce. However, despite his family's financial poverty, Bill's childhood memories were happy, marred only by the death of his mother and his older brother, Dick.

In 1948, Bill left school and began working for a small, local firm as a panel beater. 5 years later, he married Alice, his childhood sweetheart, and they moved into a small row-house close to the factory. There they raised their two children, Ian and Rose. Although money was 'tight', Bill and Alice were content. Once a week they went to the pictures and twice a week they helped at a local scout group. Then in 1970, Bill was injured in an accident at work. He sustained a severe spinal injury when a sheet of metal fell on him. The removal of a lumbar vertebra failed to restore his health, and Bill was forced to take early retirement and register as disabled. 5 years later a third child, Helen, was born.

In 1983, Bill and Alice moved to South Wales. They rented a small house in Pengelly and, with the two girls, Rose and Helen, they began the task of creating a new home for themselves. Although he was close to his parents, Ian decided to remain in the Midlands. He was settled there with his friends and his beloved football team, Aston Villa.

Bill and Alice loved their new way of life. In particular, they enjoyed the freedom and the beauty of the countryside around them and each weekend they went walking or fishing together. During the week, Bill occupied his time with part-time employment. In the summer he managed an ice-cream van and in the winter he made wooden toys for a toy shop in the town. The money he earned from these jobs helped to supplement his disability pension.

On 4 January 1987, Bill was referred to the dental hospital with a 3-month history of recurrent mouth infections, general malaise, anorexia, weight loss and shortness of breath. Following the initial dental

8. BILL

and medical assessment, a routine blood test was performed and this revealed the underlying pathology. Bill was diagnosed as having acute myeloid leukaemia and was admitted to the haematology unit. He was 53 years old.

Prior to his illness with leukaemia, Bill had been hospitalised on three separate occasions. These encounters with hospital life were brief and routine. In contrast, he now faced the prospect of prolonged hospitalisation for cytotoxic and antibiotic chemotherapy and supportive care.

Bill was a man who loved people. He was constantly concerned about the welfare of those around him. Before his illness, he looked after a couple of old-age-pensioners. Frequently, he ran errands for them or did shopping for them. When he was hospitalised with leukaemia, he transferred his attention away from his elderly neighbours and on to the staff and patients on the ward. When he was well, he liked to help care for his colleagues, either by performing small practical tasks for them or by talking to them. He also spent a lot of time with the staff, chatting to them, 'getting to know them and getting to know all their ways'.

As a result of his activities, Bill soon became a familiar figure on the ward. As his illness progressed, his bald, Gandhi-like figure was commonly seen wandering around the unit, a drip-stand at his side. Even when he was not in sight, one always knew when Bill was around due to the unfortunate whistle that his hearing-aid emitted. The whistle had a particularly piercing quality at night. Furthermore, there were also the times when Bill's batteries were running low. No longer capable of discerning the volume of his own voice, Bill talked to everyone in a loud, booming baritone.

I always enjoyed spending time with Bill. He had a warm, transparent personality and his attitude to life was unique and refreshing. Over the months of his illness, my relationship with Bill grew. We had many times of discussion together, exploring issues such as religion, hospital life, illness, death, relationships and people's attitudes and behaviours. Surprisingly, Bill rarely mentioned his wife during these conversations, although he spoke at length about his children and his dog. He also took a keen interest in my work and my social life. As we chatted together, he encouraged me to share my thoughts and ideas and my exploits. By keeping up-to-date with the things that were happening in my life, he was able to stay in touch with reality.

On the ward, Bill was notorious for his quick wit and his irrepressible sense of humour. He appeared to make a joke out of everything, regardless of the misfortune that beset him at the time. When he was receiving chemotherapy, he would laugh and joke with the nursing and medical personnel who were attending him and, even when he was afflicted with grossly debilitating side-effects from his treatment, he still made an effort to chat with his room-mates. However, underneath this happy veneer, Bill was an angry and frustrated man. He was a man battling to come to terms with leukaemia and its control over his life. If given the opportunity, he would willingly remove his mask of happiness and confide in his counsellor, divulging his struggles and fears.

I met Bill the day he was admitted to hospital, a few hours after he had been diagnosed. Not surprisingly, after having endured a barrage of medical tests at the dental hospital and received the awful news of his diagnosis and the details of his planned treatment, Bill was in a state of shock. He was also a very sick man. The following morning, I sat and chatted to Bill before I went off duty. He had slept well and was eager to talk. However, he was at an early stage in his illness and I was determined not to burden him with conversation. I deferred our meeting until the following week.

11 January 1987

It was a week since Bill's diagnosis. He had completed his first course of chemotherapy and he was now being treated with intravenous antibiotics for his chest infection.

Bill sat watching television in the quiet seclusion of his single room. In appearance, he always reminded me of a rather amiable scarecrow. He was dressed in a pair of pale green hospital pyjamas. His eyes were a blueish-grey colour and he had a tousled mop of grey woolly hair that obviously had a mind of its own.

Bill looked up when I walked into the room and smiled a greeting. His broad, face-splitting smile revealed a scanty collection of stained, yellow-brown teeth and also reopened several small cracks on his dry, scabbed lips. A trickle of blood ran down his chin. In an absent-minded gesture, Bill pulled a tissue out of his jacket pocket and dabbed at his chin.

An intravenous infusion of packed cells and normal saline was in progress, dripping rhythmically down the tubing and into a vein in Bill's left arm. A hospital locker was pulled up close to the bed. It was laden with an array of bottles, a colourful jumble of mouth-wash fluids and an assortment of fruit juice containers. The table was also loaded with boxes of tissues and trays for mouth and eye care. Bill patted the crumpled bedspread beside him and moved his legs to one side of the bed, making a space for me.

'Come and sit down,' he invited.

I sat down on the bed. As I didn't have a tape-recorder, I asked Bill if I could take notes of our conversation.

He nodded. 'Fine by me. What do you want to know?'

'Perhaps you could start by telling me what it's like to have leukaemia?' I suggested.

Bill shrugged his shoulders indifferently. 'Well, it's just a disease like any other disease. If you've got it, you've got it. You can't do anythin' about it. You just 'ave to 'ave faith in yourself to get well, and you 'ave to 'ave faith in the doctors. If you 'ave a problem, you discuss it with the doctors. You talk about it and...' Bill paused and glanced quickly at me. 'They're really good in 'ere. When I came in, they told me everythin' I needed to know. They told me all about the disease and the treatments and things. It was really interestin'. When I don't know things, I ask lots of questions, too. Like this mornin', the doctor came in with all 'is blood bottles and things, and so I asked 'im what they was for. 'E sat down and 'e told me all about 'em; 'e was really straight.'

'You like to know what's going on, don't you?' I observed.

Bill nodded. 'Yes, I do. I need to know, 'cos it 'elps me fight the disease.' He paused for a few moments and then said, 'The main thing I can do to fight the disease is do everythin' the doctors tell me to do. I mean if they said to me, "You've got stomach cancer!" I'd say, "All right, what can I do about it?" I 'ave to work with the doctors, otherwise I'll go downhill, won't I?'

'You'll go downhill?' I repeated.

'Yes.' Bill affirmed. 'The doctors know what's wrong. So I 'ave to work with 'em. I 'ave to do as I'm told. We pull together. If I'm goin' to pull through this, I've got to do my bit. I 'ave to 'ave faith in the doctors, and I 'ave to co-operate with 'em. There's no point in arguin' with 'em; they know what they're doin' and so do the nurses.... In fact, I get a lot of support and encouragement from the staff. They 'elp me do things. No, if I didn't get on with 'em, I wouldn't get anywhere. It would be a much 'arder battle to get over.' Bill spoke slowly, almost putting his thoughts together as he spoke. 'I've got to 'ave faith in what they're doin', and I 'ave to 'ave faith in God too.'

'Your faith is important to you, isn't it?' I remarked.

Bill nodded. 'Yes. You see, if you've got leukaemia and you think you're goin' to die, that's the wrong attitude to take. You've got to look at the positive side of things. Now and again, I get a bit down. So I start to think of the family, and I soon pick up again. I love 'em, even though they can be perishers at times.... No, people get ill no matter who they are, and I think, if they 'aven't got that faith in God and that encouragement from within 'emselves, they won't make it. The staff and their families can encourage 'em and it won't mean a thing. In the end, it all comes down to personal faith and positive attitude....' He paused and added as an afterthought, 'I pray to God and ask 'im to give me the strength to fight it....'

Bill moved around the bed, endeavouring to make himself comfortable. As he moved, there was a loud crack. I jumped.

'D'ya 'ear that?' Bill asked, unnecessarily. 'That was m' ankle. It never used to do that. It's all 'em drugs they're givin' me,' he informed me. 'I've got gout with all the chemo.' He leaned forward and began to massage his ankle. 'It locks sometimes.' He gave a deep sigh. 'When they told me at first, it didn't sink in at all. Even now, I feel so great, I can't quite believe that I've got leukaemia.' He laughed sardonically. 'It was a week today. But I've got faith, and I'll do what they say....'

A long silence followed, and Bill turned to stare out of the window. I thought to probe his feelings further, but instead I sat quietly. My questions remained unspoken. Bill's ankle sounded another loud crack.

'Have you had many physical problems since you started the treatment?' I enquired.

Bill shook his head. 'No, no problems really. The ankle doesn't really bother me, and I 'ad the tiredness before. The sickness bothers me a bit, but I just relax and let it pass.... No, I can't let it get me down. I've got to fight it. I've got to be positive about it, because it's all mind over matter.'

'Mind over matter?' I reflected.

'Well, I think of it, the leukaemia, then I think of m' family,' he explained. 'There's such a lot left to do, and I'm only 'alfway through m' life. I'm only 53, and there's such a lot I can do. There's such a lot of old people near us, pensioners. There's one couple up the road; I do their shoppin' for 'em.' He grinned mischievously and chuckled. 'They'll 'ave to do things for 'emselves now. It won't 'urt 'em. In fact, the walkin' will do 'em good!'

There was a brief knock at the door, and a student nurse entered the room. She smiled at Bill and said, by way of explanation, 'I'm doing drugs with Sister. Do you need anything, Bill?'

Bill shook his head. 'No thanks, love.' The student turned and walked out of the room, closing the door behind her. Bill looked up at me. 'I don't think doctors and nurses should get involved with their patients, not emotionally involved anyway.'

'You don't think they should get involved?' I repeated, wondering what had initiated this comment.

'No, I find it 'ard if the staff get too involved and they get sad. It makes me feel seriously ill. It makes me feel as though I'm goin' to give way. So I prefer it if they come straight out and tell me that they're goin' to fight it with me.' He paused and added, 'It's the same with us, the patients. We shouldn't get too involved with the staff. Now, I'm a good talker, and one of the nurses likes to come in and talk to me. She just sits and talks to me, and gradually she relaxes. I think she 'as problems at 'ome, but I'm not goin' to get involved, 'cos it puts too much pressure on us both....'

As I sat listening to Bill, I watched his facial expressions and his movements. He appeared listless and tired. Concerned for his health, I suggested that we postpone our conversation until the following morning.

12 January 1987

'...and when you've read the marking on the thermometer, you shake the mercury back down into the bulb, like this...and then, using one of these swabs, you wipe this silver bulb, the bit that goes under your tongue.... Now you try it.'

A student nurse sat by Bill's bed, instructing him on the art of reading a thermometer. Monitoring temperature was one of the skills that Bill needed to master before he could be discharged home.

Bill lay on the bed. He was unshaven, and his eyes looked bloodshot and tired. He appeared irritable as he talked to the nurse, impatiently questioning her about facets of the technique and his persistent mild pyrexia. When the teaching session was completed, the student left the room.

I sat down on the bed and asked, 'How are things, Bill?'

'I'm fed up!' he grunted. 'I 'ad a bad night last night. It was really cold, so I coughed a lot, and what with m' teeth bein' loose, it made m' gums bleed again. But the staff don't understand.' Bill gave an expansive wave in the direction of the nurse's station. 'They just came in and gave me a row for not usin' the mouthwashes. There was no need for it. I do everythin' they tell me. I eat the right food. I drink plenty and, what with this,' Bill pointed to the jumble of fruit juice containers on the top of his locker, 'and all the i.v. fluid they give me, I'm goin' to the loo all the time. Look at 'em all.' Bill nodded at the row of overflowing urine bottles, lined up against the wall. He grunted again and grumbled. 'They just don't understand. It's all the small vessels in m' mouth. They bleed real easy.' He stuck out his tongue in order to validate his explanation. 'And they keep naggin' me to clean m' mouth and use the mouthwashes.'

'How do you find the mouthwashes?' I asked.

'That's just it,' he fumed. 'I don't like the pink one! The other one's OK, but it's not really a mouthwash. Before I came in, m' doctor prescribed Betadine for me and that's what I was usin'. Anyway, now I 'ave to use this pink stuff, and m' mouth's dry as soon as I've used it.' He flopped back on to his pillows with a disconsolate expression on his face. 'And another thing:' he went on, 'one minute they say that I'm OK and I can go 'ome tomorrow. Then the next thing I know, they say m' temperature is up and I need blood because m' count is low. M' count was 10 a couple of days ago, and now it's only 2. I'm not surprised m' temp's up. It's all the stress, and m' son is stayin' with us till Saturday....' Bill shrugged his shoulders helplessly and continued, 'When Dr Edwards comes in with all 'is understudies and the pharmacist and everybody, 'e 'asn't got time to talk. It's frustratin', 'cos I need to know! I know I've got to cool down and be patient.' He grinned at the hypocrisy of his own words. 'Everythin' comes to those who wait....'

'You feel angry?' I observed.

'I'm not angry. To a certain extent, I'm annoyed, mainly because they tell me somethin' and then do somethin' different....'

After a week of treatment and inpatient care, Bill had begun to encounter a few of the problems associated with his leukaemia. His labile physical condition resulted in sudden and unexpected treatment changes. Forced to remain in hospital and receive further treatment, Bill was frustrated and agitated. He was also bewildered and confused by the seemingly contradictory information he had received from nursing and medical personnel. It was only later, when a staff nurse sat with him and explained his condition and therapy to him, that Bill was finally able to relax. In the meanwhile, I attempted to alleviate the tension by asking Bill about his family and his plans for the future.

Bill sat quietly for a few moments, considering my questions. 'I don't look too far ahead. I just think about today and the things that are goin' to 'appen today. I'm gettin' there, but it could take a long time. I don't worry, though. Worryin' doesn't 'elp. I just leave it to God....' He paused, and then conceded, 'I suppose I worry about finances. When the wife comes in to see me, I ask 'er if she's put the cheques in the bank. The bank pay all our bills, but we've got to remember to put the cheques in. I worry in case she 'asn't remembered to do that....' He shook his head. 'I don't worry about anythin' else, though. No, m' wife's the worrier. She worries about me and the little one. The older ones can look after 'emselves, but the little one doesn't understand what's 'appenin'. She's too young....'

Bill stopped talking and gazed out of the window. On the window ledge, two obese pigeons were pecking furiously at a small pile of breadcrumbs. He turned and looked at me. 'Anyway, the wife's busy gettin' the 'ouse ready for when I come 'ome. It's a cold 'ouse and so she's buyin' a portable gas fire to go at the top of the landin'.' He smiled. 'It'll really warm the place up. The social worker's been in as well, and she's pushin' the council to come and put central 'eatin' in. We can't 'ave the gas on all night. It's not safe, you see, particularly if there's a draught. But the council don't care....

Despite his temperature, Bill expected to be discharged the following day. Unfortunately, throughout the day, his temperature continued to rise, and by the evening, he had also developed a sore throat. The next morning, Bill was detained in hospital and started on a new course of intravenous antibiotics.

For the next 5 weeks, Bill remained in hospital. A severe throat infection later developed into pneumonia and then into septicaemia. His second course of cytotoxic chemotherapy was postponed. During the weeks of illness, Bill experienced considerable weight loss and developed a widespread erythema. Eventually, after prolonged antibiotic chemotherapy, Bill's condition began to improve. It was the middle of February.

17 February 1987

The air in Bill's hospital room was hot and stuffy. Sunlight streamed in through the windows, augmenting the heat generated by the hospital boilers. A collection of cards and children's drawings was taped to the wall behind his bed. There were also more cards and flowers on the window-sill. The characteristic array of medicine pots, boxes of tissues, bottles of mouthwash fluid and high protein drinks cluttered the top of the bedside locker. On another table, a fan whirled noisily, blowing gusts of warm air around the room.

Bill lay quietly on top of the bed, resting. He was dressed in a pair of green hospital pyjamas. Typically, the trouser bottoms were several inches too short for his long, bony legs. Bill's body looked thin and gaunt. His eyes and cheeks had a hollow, sunken appearance. He was bald, and his brown, mottled skin was covered in scars and open sores.

I switched the tape-recorder on. In a quiet, husky voice, Bill began to describe his experiences of the past few weeks.

'After I finished the first leukaemia therapy, they waited for m' temperature to stay down. One day, they'd tell me that I could go 'ome, and then the next day they'd come round again and say, "We're goin' to keep you in." That 'appened again and again and again, but I was determined not to let it get me down.' He paused. 'It's 6 weeks yesterday since m' diagnosis. When I come in, I was very weak, I was full of leukaemia, and now that's much better. But Dr Roberts can't quite put 'is finger on what's been wrong with me.' Bill glanced at me and explained. 'It's probably because 'e 'asn't read m' notes.'

'He hasn't read your notes?' I repeated.

Bill shook his head. 'No 'e 'asn't.... At the moment, 'e's concerned about the state of m' body. That's why 'e's keepin' me in. But I only want a few weeks at 'ome.' Bill shrugged his shoulders helplessly. 'It isn't m' throat as such, that can be treated at 'ome. It's the tempera-ture. But the treatment's workin', and it's goin' down now.' He grinned broadly. 'Deep down, I feel that the doctors might let me go 'ome for a week or two, just to get some weight on these legs.' To illustrate his point, Bill lifted his right leg off the bed and pulled up his trouser leg. His calf was thin and emaciated. He pushed his trouser leg down again and gently lowered his leg on to the counter-pane. 'Anyway, if the doctor said to me, "Bill, I'm sorry, but you've got to stop in", I'd accept it... OK, I'd feel down in the mouth for a few hours, but I'd soon be back to normal, pullin' the nurses' legs and 'avin' a joke with 'em....'

'You find that humour helps?' I rejoined.

'Well it's what you make of it, isn't it? I mean, if I can laugh and joke with all the nurses and doctors, it 'elps me. If I lie 'ere all miserable, it doesn't do me any good at all, does it? I've got to make a laugh out of things.' He smiled. 'I pull Dr Sandra's leg, somethin' terrible. She doesn't mind, and when the others do their rounds in the mornin' I 'ave a little joke with 'em. Well, I've got to be able to relax, 'aven't I? If I'm all tensed up, it doesn't 'elp me. I've got to relax.' Bill frowned and turned towards me. 'But the doctors are concerned about the infection in m' left lung. I've 'ad it for donkey's years and it doesn't do no 'arm. It just makes a grumblin' sound, that's all. But the doctors, they worry about it. Same with the cough. I cough every mornin'. Well, it does the lungs good to be pumped around a bit. Anyway, the doctors got the physio to come in and see me for quite a few weeks.'

He paused. 'They even worry about m' skin; it's gone brown and it's peelin'.' He shook his head in disbelief. 'I don't worry about it, 'cos it was the drugs that done it. The Boss come in to see me about it. 'E apologised to me and said, "I'm very sorry about your legs." 'E said, "If there was anythin' we could do to stop this sort of thing 'appenin', we'd do it. But it just 'appens, and it's unfortunate."' Bill shrugged his shoulders again to convey his lack of concern.

The topic of conversation altered. We began to discuss Bill's war against weight. Since his diagnosis he had lost 4 stones. His initial chemotherapy reduced his appetite by promoting nausea and vomiting, dry mouth and taste changes. A subsequent series of painful throat and mouth infections then prevented him from eating solid food. Indeed, at one time, he was unable to swallow his own saliva. Although Bill's mouth was much improved, eating was still painful for him. At lunchtime that day, I watched Bill struggle through a few mouthfuls of jelly and ice-cream. His special fortified diet remained on the tray, untouched. After lunch, a student nurse gently cleaned his mouth before recording the meagre details of his 'dietary intake' on the chart at the bottom of his bed.

'You don't seem to worry about your illness, Bill.' I remarked.

Bill grinned. 'Well, I'm not a person to worry about being ill. The only thing I worry about is losing weight, and I know that if I could get 'ome for about 3 or 4 days and get some good 'ome cookin' inside me, I'd be all right. You can't beat 'ome cookin': good thick stews, solid food.... The food in 'ere is OK, but it's badly presented, and I don't like the stuff they put in m' drink either. It's too sweet!* But I 'ave started to eat again. I can eat very soft food and fluid.' He smiled proudly and announced, 'I ate a whole poached egg for breakfast this mornin'! But m' mouth is still sore. It 'urts when I swallow, so I 'ave to mash everythin' up....'

While undergoing treatment, Bill was forced to relinquish his normal life. He also had to give up his associate roles of husband, parent and community member. With his past experience of illness and disability, Bill was adept at coping with his disease. However, after 6 weeks of intensive cytotoxic chemotherapy, he was tired and disheartened.

---

* In order to fortify Bill's diet, the dietician advised the addition of Caloreen, a high calorie supplement, to Bill's water. Bill disliked the taste of the Caloreen and refused to drink his water.

He wanted desperately to go home and live normally again. He talked about illness and the changes it had wrought upon his life

'I miss m' old life, because deep down the family comes first.... I'm in 'ere. I'm safe. I'm in good 'ands. I know m' wife's all right, otherwise she'd 've phoned in to let me know what was wrong.' He glanced quickly at me. 'But then again, I get m' visitors from 'ome and I ask 'em if anythin' 'as 'appened. "No!" they say. A few days later, the wife'll say, "Oh, our Ian phoned!" I get the news a few days later than normal.... One day m' mother collapsed while she was out shoppin'. They didn't tell me about it for a long time after, in case I worried about it! Well, there was nothin' I could do. I could think about it, but I couldn't do anythin'.' Bill shook his head sadly. 'They should've told me straight away, 'cos I like to know when one of the family 'as 'ad a bump or an odd mo'. What do you think?'

As I was reluctant to enter into a discussion on the subject, I altered the direction of our conversation and asked him about his younger daughter, Helen. 'How's Helen these days?"

Bill's face brightened. 'She's growin' up fast. She's 12 now, and she 'as to be up by 7.30 to go to school. Every mornin', after breakfast, she goes off to meet 'er pals up the road.' Bill smiled. 'She's into everythin' and she likes to keep records. It's funny, she takes all m' menu cards and puts 'em in a scrapbook. She 'as a diary as well, and she likes to keep a record of everythin' that's 'appenin' in the world....' Bill hesitated and frowned. 'Since I've been ill though, she's been a lot quieter. She doesn't ask as many questions.'

During the initial 6 weeks of Bill's hospitalisation, Helen visited her father only once. Bill was distressed by Helen's refusal to visit him in hospital.

'Trouble is, she don't like comin' in 'ere. She came in a few weeks back and when she got 'ome, she said that she didn't want to come in again. I can accept that, 'cos children are a bit wary of 'ospitals and I don't want to put 'er off... She sends me cards, though. She made me a big moon-shaped one at school. It was pink, and it 'ad a big red nose, a wide mouth and writin' on it. It looked a real treat, particularly for someone like me who can't swallow.' Bill smiled at the irony of his situation. 'I do worry about 'er, though. The older ones can look after 'emselves, but Helen's only little and she don't really understand.'

'Sometimes children understand more than we think!' I challenged.

'You're right.' Bill conceded. 'Helen was very close to m' dad. Well, all the children were close to 'im.' He laughed and explained, 'He let 'em do anythin', go into all the cupboards, go all over the 'ouse. I told 'im that 'e shouldn't spoil 'em, but 'e never listened. 'E 'ad an 'ouse in the Midlands, and we used to go over fairly often, till we moved to Pengelly....'

'So Helen knew her grandfather quite well?' I interjected.

Bill nodded. 'Yes, they were very close. Anyway, 'e died 2 years ago. I was with 'im when 'e died. 'E slept most of the mornin'. 'E wasn't aware of much; 'e was in a sort of coma. At one point, 'e called for Dick.' Bill glanced at me and explained, 'Dick died when 'e was 27, from cancer of the larynx.... Before dad went, I give 'im a clout on the 'eart, and 'e came round for a while. Later, the doctor came and said that 'e was dead, and so I went down and told the family. Before they came to look at 'im, I laid 'im out and made 'im look presentable. I'd given 'im a wash and shave earlier that mornin', so I just put 'is teeth in and combed 'is 'air.... Helen came up with the wife, but she didn't say anythin'. She just looked at 'er grandad and then went out again. She 'eld it all in....'

* * *

A few weeks after our second meeting, Bill was discharged home. Twice a week, he returned to the hospital to have his blood tested. Subsequently, he was readmitted for the insertion of a Hickman line. After the procedure, Bill remained in hospital overnight, and he was discharged home the following morning. After several weeks of convalescence at home, Bill was admitted for a second course of chemotherapy.

13 April 1987

It was a week before Easter. Currently, Bill was receiving his second course of chemotherapy. Bill spotted me in the corridor as I walked past his room. He waved wildly and called, 'Hello! Come in and 'ave a chat.' As I entered the room, Bill pointed to the armchair beside his bed and said, 'You can sit 'ere.' Obediently, I sat down.

Bill sat cross-legged on the bed; his legs hidden under the crumpled green counterpane. Although his face was flushed, he looked fit and well. During his time at home, he had gained a stone in weight, and his body had lost its scarred, emaciated appearance. His hair had also started to grow.

Although Bill had been admitted only the previous day, his bed space looked very homely. Two of Helen's drawings were Sellotaped to the wall behind the bed and a bowl of daffodils stood on the table near the window. As usual, a familiar jumble of bottles, glasses, boxes of tissues and medicine pots lay scattered on top of the bedside table and locker.

'So, what's been happening to you?' I asked.

'Well, as you know,' Bill began, 'I went 'ome for a few days and then I came in again on Friday for some blood tests. They found out that m' blood was affected again, so I 'ad to stay in, and the doctors started me on some new leukaemia treatment.' He gave a wry smile. 'The new treatment's all right. I've 'ad no side-effects and I'm eatin' m' food and everythin'.' Bill paused and frowned. 'Trouble is, last Thursday I was told that I 'ad to 'ave another course of this new drug to try and finish it off.' He glanced at me and explained, 'You see, there's only a minute amount of the leukaemia left in the bone. Now, if I'd started the treatment a week or so sooner, I'd 've 'ad time to get over any side-effects and I'd 've been 'ome for Easter. But now, because they started it late, I won't be able to go 'ome for Easter without 'avin' to come back every day for check-ups.' Bill lowered his voice and grumbled, 'They keep sayin' to me, "You can go 'ome," and then I find that I can't. It's annoyin', very annoyin', 'cos I build me 'opes up for goin' 'ome and then all of a sudden, I'm down again.... And another thing, we've got six or so people comin' this weekend. There's m' son, m' brother and 'is wife and their son, and m' sister and 'er 'usband.... It'll be a real family gatherin'. The wife gets a bit agitated in case I'm not 'ome for Easter....' Bill shrugged his shoulders in a gesture of helpless frustration before resuming his tirade against the staff. 'I wish they'd do what they say they're goin' to do and not mess about!'

'In what way?' I asked.

'Well, like last Thursday, I could've started the treatment, but the nurses said that they didn't know anythin' about it. The drug was in the cupboard, ready to use. One of the nurses got told off today! The doctor told 'er off and...' Bill's voice trailed off and he peered out into the corridor to check that no one could overhear our conversation. Then he bent forward so that his head was close to mine and whispered loudly, 'The doctor told 'er off. 'E said to 'er, "What's all the fuss about then?" She went bright red!' Bill grinned roguishly. 'But I think, if you're goin' to do a job, you should get on with it and get it over with. I mean, I don't mind what they do as long as they don't make me 'ang around and waste m' time. I mean, what's the time now?'

I looked at my watch. 'Nearly ten past two,' I informed him.

'Ten past two!' he spluttered. 'The treatment should've been up at 12 o'clock. They can do it in 'alf an hour. Although, if they run it in too fast, it gives me an 'eadache and it takes a while for the 'eadache to wear off. It's 'ighly toxic, you see....' He paused briefly and then added, 'If I go 'ome tomorrow, I've got to come back every day for tests and things. But it's too late now anyway.'

'Too late?' I prompted.

'Yeah, too late for Easter. If I go 'ome, I've still got to come in every other day for tests and things,' he explained. 'And that's another thing. I think they should let me 'ave m' blood tests nearer 'ome. We 'ave to travel 40 miles, 20 miles 'ere and then 20 miles back. That's a bloody long way just to 'ave a blood test, and it creates more work for 'em. They could be doin' somethin' for the people who really need treatin'....'

Evidently, Bill was bewildered and angry. The delay in the administration of his chemotherapy, the apparent inconsistencies in the information given to him by nursing and medical personnel, the broken promises regarding his discharge, all combined to create within him a feeling of tension and frustration. In addition, his desire to regain control of his circumstances and his growing familiarity with the treatments and the daily ward routine meant that he was becoming less tolerant of hospital procedures which he considered to be unnecessary and intrusive. Fortunately, Bill still maintained a high regard for the hospital staff and, moreover, the insertion of the Hickman line had raised his morale. The line was physically and psychologically beneficial. It not only eradicated the physical discomfort he formerly experienced with intravenous therapy, but it also enabled him to participate more actively in care. However, in general, Bill's expanding knowledge of hospital life made him sensitive to the injustices common to the inpatient and more willing to voice his complaints.

Bill glanced quickly towards the door and the deserted corridor. 'This mornin', I pressed the buzzer and I asked 'em about the treatment. Jenny came, and I said to 'er, "I 'aven't got anythin' besides the leukaemia drugs, 'ave I?" She said, "No!" "What about the platelets?" I said. "Oh yes, them!" she said.' Bill shook his head in disbelief. 'She'd forgotten about the platelets!'

As Bill's angry outburst continued, I began to feel increasingly uncomfortable. In an attempt to change the subject, I commented on Bill's obvious weight gain. 'You seem to have gained a bit of weight since you went home.'

'Yes, I 'ave,' Bill acknowledged. 'Well, I'd lost a lot of weight. I was 12 stones when I come in, and I went down to nearly 8. Now, I'm just over 9 stones. They weighed me this mornin'.'

'So it's climbing back?' I congratulated him.

'Yep, it's climbin' back.' Bill grinned happily. 'I've not got m' top teeth, but I can still eat m' food. Yesterday, I 'ad roast beef and Yorkshire puddin'. I didn't eat it all. Well, there's no salt in it.... No salt in the Yorkshire puddin', none in the cabbage, none in the potato. Everythin's a bit tasteless.'

I spotted a salt-cellar partially hidden behind a 'get well' card on his locker top. 'So you've brought your own packet of salt!' I observed.

Bill grinned mischievously. 'Yes, I've got m' own packet of salt. But, apart from the salt, the food isn't too bad in 'ere. It isn't pureed now, but it's still not as good as it is at 'ome!'

Concerned that Bill would resume his tirade against the staff, I asked him about his treatment. 'How's the treatment going?'

Bill nodded happily. 'Oh, it's much better now. The new treatment's very toxic, but with it goin' through the 'ickman line, it 'as a better flow. It feels easier and it goes through the system easier. The 'ickman line's a lot more pleasant.' He grinned. 'I don't 'ave needles in me 'ands all the time. Me 'ands are free to do what I want. It's no problem at 'ome either, 'cos the district nurse comes in to 'elp me. I get the stuff ready and then she 'elps me do it. When I was 'ome, she came in every day for about a month or so, and then she just popped in now and again to see 'ow I was gettin' on. I was concerned about flushin' it, but I only need to do that once a week, which isn't so bad.'

'Can you do that?' I asked.

Bill nodded proudly. 'Yep! I did it today. Well, I didn't 'ave to flush it, 'cos that 'ad already been done. But I dressed it.' Bill pointed to the space by his bed. 'I did it there. Anne watched me to make sure I didn't go wrong and it went quite easy, no trouble at all.' Bill lay back on the pillows looking pleased with himself.

'You're getting quite the expert now,' I observed

Bill grinned. 'Yes, I am. I can even tell when the doctor's goin' to do somethin' wrong with the drip.' He winked at me. 'If there isn't a three-way tap on the line, I let 'em off lightly, because they've got to put a needle in to put the antibiotics up and it's a bit more fiddly.' He grinned again. 'They asked me to talk to one of the relatives about it.... It was a gentleman. Anne brought 'im round to see me so that 'e could 'ave a look at the line because 'is wife's goin' to 'ave one. 'E asked me if it felt all right and I said, "Yes, and it's all right goin' 'ome, 'cos it winds up under the pad and you put a piece of gauze over it and tape it down. You don't notice it."' He glanced at me quickly and added, 'The only time I notice anythin' is when I've got a bag 'ooked up. I 'ave to be careful when I turn over, 'cos it does pull a bit.'

Bill rubbed his cheek and carefully removed a small piece of dry skin. 'But it's OK with the coat-'n'-hat stand. I get used to 'im after a while. In fact, the last time I come off the drip, I kept on lookin' for 'im!' Bill chuckled and then, becoming more serious, he added, 'These doctors, they all 'ave a different opinion.... Some months ago, Dr Edwards said there was only 5% of the leukaemia left in the bone.... Then this mornin', the other doctor said that there was more 'n that, and that there was some in the bloodstream as well.' Bill cleared his throat. 'I don't see 'ow the body could produce more in the marrow bone with none bein' produced in the normal blood....'

'It's confusing, isn't it?' I agreed.

'It is! I mean, yesterday they told me that I only needed 4 days of treatment, and yet I still needed 7 days. Then they told me that I'd misunderstood 'em! I knew I 'adn't, 'cos when you've got to 'ave treatment that's goin' to knock you back, you listen, you listen 'ard.

Anyway, if I'm not sure what the doctor's been sayin' when 'e comes round, I just ask the nurse that's with 'im to come back later and tell me what 'e's said.'

Feeling threatened by Bill's frustration, I again tried to redirect the conversation. I asked questions and probed, but Bill refused to be drawn into the discussion. He had other things on his mind.

'You know Lorraine died, don't you?' Bill asked.

I nodded. 'Yes.'

'I think I can 'ear 'er callin' sometimes at night and in the day. When I 'ear 'er, I think to m'self, "What does she want?"'

'Does it disturb you?' I enquired.

Bill shook his head. 'No, it doesn't, 'cos I know she's at rest.... I feel sorry for the rest of the family, though, 'cos they've lost somebody that they loved. But she'd suffered for years from various things....' He grunted and added as an afterthought, 'It wasn't the leukaemia what killed 'er; it was 'er 'eart. But she wouldn't relax....'

'She was a frightened lady,' I commented.

'Aye,' Bill acknowledged, 'she was very frightened.' He altered his position on the bed, trying to make himself comfortable. 'It's a pity that there wasn't somebody in the family, somebody like yourself, that could talk to 'er. I couldn't talk to 'er. I could talk to 'er 'usband, but all I could say to 'er was, "And 'ow's Lorraine today?" and "Oh! You seem better today!" She used to be up-and-down, you see.'

'Up-and-down?' I repeated.

Bill ignored my comment and continued, 'It depends on the mind of the person who's 'avin' the treatment, doesn't it? I mean, she 'ad a son and a daughter, and she was only 38, wasn't she?'

'36,' I corrected.

Bill raised his eyebrows. 'Really! She couldn't 'elp 'erself, and there was nobody to 'elp 'er. As I told you, I couldn't talk to 'er....'

Bill appeared preoccupied with Lorraine's death. In the past, he had witnessed the death of family members, friends and patient colleagues. I wondered if these deaths had been as traumatic as Lorraine's recent death. I asked Bill to describe his previous encounters with death.

'The first person I saw die was in 'ospital in Coventry. A man died in the bed next to mine. The doctor went to 'ave a look at 'im and, as 'e walked away, the man stopped breathin'. I called a nurse and said, "I think 'e's gone."'

'Did that experience upset you?' I interjected.

'No, it didn't worry me,' Bill retorted. 'I'd seen dead people before. M' mum died when I was little. Every mornin' before I went to school, I used to go into the front room and give 'er a kiss on the forehead. It didn't bother me 'til they took 'er out of the 'ouse. They took 'er to the cemetery....'

'You felt that you'd lost her,' I suggested.

'I did, aye!' Bill affirmed. 'It was the only time I cried. One night, I went to the cemetery to look for 'er grave, but I couldn't find it.... Later, I found out that it was No. 43, but I never went back....'

'Would you go back now?' I asked.

'Would I go back?' Bill lay back on his pillows and stared at the wall in front of him, as he considered my question. Then he looked back at me and announced, 'No, we should let 'er rest. She died young; she was 47 or 48. 48 I think. She died of white-leg; that comes of 'avin' babies and doin' work straight away. She wouldn't rest you see. She always thought of the family before 'erself....'

We sat in silence for a few moments, then I asked Bill about suffering.

'Bill, do you feel that you've suffered during your illness?'

He smiled quietly and repeated my question. 'Have I suffered? Well, that's the $64 000 question. To a certain extent, yes, I 'ave suffered, but I know I can fight the illness.... I suppose I ask, "Why am I sufferin'? What 've I done to deserve it?" But then at the same time, I know God is 'elpin' me to fight it.' He turned and looked out of the window. 'But it's 'ard bein' in 'ere. It's 'ard watchin' other people suffer when I know that I can't do anythin' to 'elp.... I feel sorry for a lot of the people 'ere. They seem so ill, and there's no one to 'elp 'em.... All I can recommend is faith, but I can't give that to people. I can explain to 'em 'ow I feel, but if they don't believe in God, I can't make 'em believe....'

8. BILL

He moved his position again. 'No, for me, sufferin' is 'avin' to watch somebody else suffer that I can't 'elp....'

'Bill, you said that you sometimes ask the question, "Why am I suffering?" Do you try to identify the cause of your illness?'

Bill shrugged his shoulders indifferently. 'Yes, but I don't think it's my fault. It's just somethin' that's in me already. It's like 'avin' cancer; it's there already, isn't it? It just 'as to be triggered off by somethin'. And this leukaemia, this cancer of the blood, it's just somethin' that I've got to bear.' He paused and then added philosophically, 'I've got to put up with it until it's put right. I've just got to ask God to 'elp me get better. I've got to 'ave faith....'

Bill and I talked on into the afternoon. We discussed our individual plans for Easter and for the summer holidays. As I took my leave, Bill handed me a crumpled sheet of paper. On it was written the following four lines of poetry:

> On top of old satan
> with the Lord at my side,
> I've conquered temptation
> and now I am free.

Apparently, Bill had composed the verse earlier that day; however, he didn't know how to continue the poem and so he asked me to do it for him.

* * *

I never completed the poem, and I never saw Bill again. 10 days later, he died from septicaemia. It felt strange going back on to the unit after his death, knowing that he was no longer there. For months, he had been almost a permanent inpatient, and now only the memory of him lingered.

* * * * *

9. *Anne*

ANNE GRAINGER WAS A QUIET, UNASSUMING WOMAN. SHE WAS WELL-educated and articulate, and she spoke in a soft, gentle voice. She was a tall and slender woman, and she had short, mid-brown hair which was cut in a page-boy style. She dressed simply and carefully, usually in a plain skirt and blouse. She wore no make-up.

Anne was 35 years old. She was married and had two children, a 15-year-old girl called Jessica and a 9-year-old boy called Christopher. Anne's husband, John, was a schoolteacher. He taught geography to students at a local secondary school.

Before her marriage, Anne worked as an English teacher at a local junior school. However, when Jessica was born, she stopped work to become a full-time mum and homemaker. The decision was a fortuitous one for, when Christopher was born, he was found to have a congenital heart defect. Although his condition was stable, he was susceptible to chest infections and needed frequent medical help. Each winter, for instance, he was hospitalised with pneumonia. Aware of the serious nature of his condition, Anne devoted much of her time and energy to his care.

It was the end of the summer in 1985, and Anne had been feeling unwell for several weeks. She had a persistent throat infection which 'came and went all the time'. Although her friends commented that she wasn't looking well, Anne didn't bother going to the doctor. Instead she began to treat herself at home, hoping that her infections would disappear on their own.

By September, Anne felt awful. She was constantly tired and had no energy. She knew that she wasn't well, but she couldn't identify the problem. She speculated that she 'had picked up something in hospital'. For 2 weeks, Christopher had been hospitalised with pneumonia, and Anne had stayed on the children's ward with him. Unable to shake off the heavy cold that she had developed, she reluctantly went to see her doctor.

Dr Mayers couldn't find anything wrong with her. After a brief physical examination, he dismissed her saying, 'Oh, it's just a virus.'

Although she told him about the fatigue, the sore throats and the severe headaches that were troubling her, he made a diagnosis of sinusitis and sent her home with a prescription for antibiotics. It was Friday morning.

Over the weekend, Anne began to feel worse, and on Monday she phoned Dr Mayers in desperation. Once again, he dismissed her complaints and said, 'Well, it's a virus and these viruses take months to go away.' Feeling disheartened and confused, Anne tried to diagnose herself. She picked up a medical textbook from the public library and then tried to locate her symptoms in the book.

On Wednesday, Anne went to see her dentist. She had developed a tooth abscess and was suffering sharp, stabbing pains in her jaw. During the dental consultation, the dentist remarked that Anne wasn't looking well and that she seemed very pale. He asked her how she was feeling, and she told him that she'd been waking up in the night with her nightdress wringing wet. Greatly concerned by her condition, the dentist contacted Dr Mayers and arranged for Anne to have a blood test later that afternoon.

The following morning, Dr Mayers arrived at Anne's house. Alarmed by his unexpected call, Anne realised that something was seriously wrong. The doctor came into the house, sat down and said, 'They want you to go to the hospital. Your blood is very low and you need a transfusion.'

Anne expected to be discharged home after the transfusion. Instead she underwent a barrage of blood tests and a bone marrow biopsy. She was then taken aside and told the devastating news that she had leukaemia.

Following her diagnosis, Anne was transferred to the regional haematology centre and admitted to Rhiannon Ward. Reluctantly, she began treatment. She was lucky. Her leukaemia responded well to therapy and after only two courses of chemotherapy, she went into remission. It was December 1985.

Having persuaded the doctors to delay the administration of consolidation and maintenance chemotherapy until 'after the holidays', Anne spent Christmas at home with her family. Later, in the New Year, preparations for a bone marrow transplant were initiated. Once again, Anne was fortunate. Preliminary investigations revealed that

Anne's two sisters, Amy and Geraldine, were both suitable donors. Incredibly, each one was a perfect match. Unable to choose between them, Anne asked her sisters to make the decision for her. After consulting together they decided that Amy would act as the donor, as she was single and had no dependants, while Geraldine, a wife and mother of two children, would look after Jessica and Christopher during the transplant.

The transplant was performed in July 1986. The operation went smoothly and without complications. The donor marrow grafted and 3 weeks later Anne was discharged home to begin the long, slow recovery.

* * *

In June 1987, almost a year after her transplant, Anne's marrow was functioning normally. She had regained much of her former strength and vitality and was able to resume her many duties as wife and mother. Once a month, she attended the outpatient clinic for a routine blood test and a medical consultation.

I met Anne for the first time at one of her clinic appointments. The morning clinic was busy and Anne had a long wait ahead of her. After chatting for almost an hour, I asked Anne if she would be prepared to compose a written account of her illness experiences. Anne agreed readily and we parted company.

A few weeks later, I arrived on the ward for duty. A large brown envelope was handed to me by the staff nurse. It contained Anne's written brief. At 1 o'clock in the morning, all the chores were complete and I was able to retreat to the relative peace of the sister's office, armed with a cup of tea and Anne's report.

The brief was only three pages long, and it did not take long to read. Anne wrote clearly and succinctly. She described the events of her illness in chronological order and then explored the impact of her disease upon herself and her family. In general, her illness was unremarkable; however, midway through her account, Anne described how she received prayer for healing. Apparently, prior to her transplant, the elders of her church had anointed her with oil and prayed for her. Curious about the details of her experience, I contacted Anne the following evening and arranged an interview at her home.

---

10 August 1987

Anne lived in a small, semi-detached brick house on the outskirts of Bridgeport. The house was situated in a quiet neighbourhood. There was a small strip of garden at the front of the property and this was surrounded by a low, red-brick wall. Apart from a narrow, somewhat barren flower bed that extended along the front of the house, the garden was given over to grass. Judging by the number of divots of turf missing from the lawn and the tell-tale football lying half-hidden behind a small bush near the front door, the garden was a favourite domain of Christopher and his friends.

Inside the house, the rooms were decorated and furnished quietly and tastefully. Anne showed me into the lounge and I sat down on a large, very comfortable sofa, covered in a rather ancient tweed. Anne sat facing me in an old rocking chair. Between us stood a low, oak coffee table, upon which I placed my tape-recorder. Anne handed me a large mug of hot tea.

As we began chatting, I asked Anne to tell me about her diagnosis. In her soft, low voice, Anne recounted the details of her initial illness, describing her visits to the doctor and the final trip to the hospital for the alleged 'transfusion'.

'A couple of doctors asked me a lot of questions, but I still wasn't particularly concerned. I thought, "Why don't they just get on with it and let me go home?" Then they did a bone marrow. They told me, "This just shows why you're anaemic," or something like that. About half an hour later, they called me into the office. The nurse was there, and she told me that I had to go to another hospital, and at this point I started worrying. I thought, "Gosh, there must be something wrong." But I didn't realise what it was going to be.'

'Was your husband with you?' I asked.

Anne smiled sadly at the memory. 'No,' she replied, 'I was alone. John had taken the children to stay with a friend.... I was called into the office and the doctor told me what it was. I couldn't believe it. I felt as though I'd been shot or something. It came as a real shock.'

I hesitated and then asked, 'Did you know anything about leukaemia?'

Anne looked up at me. 'Well, I'd heard about leukaemia. I knew it was a cancer of the blood, but that was all I knew. When I was told what I had, I thought, "Well, this is it. I'm going to die." I just didn't know what was going to happen. I didn't know what they could do, really.'

'Were the doctors able to explain things to you?'

Anne shook her head and turned away. 'No. They weren't very nice, actually. The doctors there didn't seem to know how to tell me. It was as though they'd never told anyone before. The doctor just came in and said, "We've got the results of your bone marrow test." I said, "Oh, yes. What is it?" He said, "It's bad, very bad." I said, "What on earth is it?" He said, "You've got leukaemia." I was stunned. I said, "Surely not! I can't believe it!" He nodded and said, "Yes." I can remember every word I said. I said, "But I can't be ill. I haven't got time to be ill myself. My little boy's not well." Anne glanced quickly at me and explained, 'My little boy, Christopher, was born with a heart condition, and he gets quite ill in the winter with his chest. He gets pneumonia and things. None of my relatives live down here, so if I'm ill my children have got no-one to look after them.' Anne paused, appearing to relive the horror of her diagnosis.

'Then what happened?' I prompted.

Returning to her story, Anne replied, 'The doctor said, "Life can be very hard, can't it?" I said, "What happens now?" He said, "Well, we want you to go to the General for treatment." I said, "What sort of treatment?" He said, "Chemotherapy." I asked him, "What's that like?" and he said, "It's horrible. It makes you ill." So I said, "Well, what if I don't go?" and he said, "You've got 6 weeks to live." I said, "Well, I'd better go, then!"'

'How did you feel at that point?'

Anne frowned, trying to recapture the turmoil of her emotions. 'Well, my heart was thumping away. I was shaking inside. I didn't know what to think. I could hardly believe it. I didn't dream there was anything seriously wrong with me. I thought it was something simple. I never thought anything like that would happen to me. It's always someone else. But anyway, I was packed off in an ambulance almost straight away. Oh, John came before I left, and they told him. He was almost as shocked as I was.' Anne hesitated, taking a few moments to collect her thoughts. 'I went off in the ambulance, and John followed us in the car. The man in the ambulance was so nice.

He said, "What's the matter, love?" I told him. I said, "I've got leukaemia." He said, "Ahh. Don't worry, love. They can cure that these days. Don't worry about it." He was so kind. He made me feel much better straight away. He chatted to me the whole way down to the hospital.'

'Tell me what happened next,' I encouraged.

'When I got there, I had to go on to Llewellyn Ward, because Rhiannon Ward was full. I was given a bed and then Dr Purvis came to see me, and he explained the situation. He was very kind and he helped me to get over the shock. He let me see that there was hope, that they could do something about it. He told me all about the treatments and everything. He told me about getting into remission.' Anne glanced at me quickly and explained, 'I didn't know what it meant to be in remission, and so he talked all about that. When I heard that there was an 80% chance of remission, I thought, "Oh, I'll be one of them."' Anne grinned.

'So you started treatment?' I suggested.

Anne nodded. 'Yes, and they gave me some penicillin to clear up this abscess on my tooth.' Anne opened her mouth wide and pointed at the offending molar. She closed her mouth and then continued, 'I was in for a week and then I went home.' She chuckled. 'I thought I was going to be stuck in hospital for months on end. I didn't realise that I would be able to go home. So I went in on the Friday, I started treatment the following Wednesday and then I went home that weekend. I had the pumps first.'

'The pumps,' I repeated.

'Yes.' Anne gave an affirmative nod. 'They were no trouble. I thought, "This is easy!" Then they told me I could go home. I was really surprised. I'd had 3 days with the pump and then 2 days with the nasty red injections. I can't even remember what they were.' Anne looked at me inquiringly.

'Adriamycin,' I suggested.

'Adria-mycin. That's it.' Anne nodded again. 'They weren't very nice. They made me feel pretty lousy. But when I finished them, I went home and I stayed in bed for a couple of days and I was all right again.' She paused and added, 'After the first lot of treatment, I felt very tired and weak. While my blood was going down, I had to go back to the hospital for blood tests every day. In those days, I had to go up to the haematology lab on the second floor. One day, I remember, I got up to the first floor and I just couldn't walk any more. I had to sit down. John was with me, and he had to go and get a wheelchair for me and take me the rest of the way....'

'Apart from the tiredness, how were you?' I asked.

'Well, I used to get these infections. About 7–10 days after I finished the treatment, I'd get an infection and I had to go in to Rhiannon. I used to get these blood infections. What are they called?'

'Septicaemia,' I supplied.

Anne repeated the name. 'Septicaemia...and those dreadful sore throats. My throat used to be so sore. I used to have ulcers all over my mouth and tongue. It was dreadful. I could hardly swallow.' Anne winced at the memory. 'My hands were swollen as well. They were swollen and red. They looked awful and I didn't know what to do with them. Anyway, I'd be in for about a week or so and then I'd go home for another week and then I'd go back in again and they'd start me off with another course of treatment.'

'It was one cycle after another, wasn't it?'

Anne nodded. 'Yes.' Then glancing over at me, she confided, 'I didn't think I would mind about losing my hair. I just wanted to get well. But when my hair did fall out, I didn't like it. I couldn't bear to look at myself in the mirror without my wig on, so I used to wear it most of the time, except when I was in the bath.' She grinned mischievously. 'When I was feeling better, Jessica and I used to go out on shopping expeditions together or out for a meal somewhere. Normally, Jessica used to love these trips, but she didn't like coming with me if it was windy in case my wig blew off. She made sure I wore a coat with a hood.' Anne's eyes sparkled in reminiscence.

Taking Anne back to the details of her treatment, I said, 'You went into remission quite quickly, didn't you?'

Anne nodded. 'Yes. I was visiting the ward after my second course of chemotherapy. I'd just come out of the lift and Dr Purvis and Dr Barnard were standing together just outside Rhiannon. Dr Purvis smiled when he saw me and said, "Ah, Mrs Grainger, I've got good news for you. You're in remission!"' Anne smiled.

'Were you expecting it?' I enquired.

'I wasn't surprised because I felt so well, but really I didn't know when to expect it, so it was lovely.' Anne smiled again and then continued, 'Anyway, he told me that I had to come in for more treatment, and I remember asking him, "Can you give me the treatments so that I don't have to be in for Christmas?"' Anne paused. 'They gave me the treatment just before Christmas and then I was in again for New Year.' Anne paused again and then said, 'I was one of the fortunate ones. I got into remission pretty quickly.'

'One of the fortunate ones?' I reflected.

'Yes, there were one or two of the others who also got into remission after a couple of courses of chemotherapy...but I think it was very wise of them to give me the extra treatment afterwards and then the extra course of half-strength chemotherapy.' Anne paused and then went on, 'A man from our church had leukaemia at the same time as I did. I think he had two courses of chemotherapy and then when he came out of remission, they couldn't get him into it again....'

The new life of illness proved difficult for Anne's whole family. Sharing the emotional and psychosocial burden of leukaemia, they suffered the pain and the hardships associated with the disease. I asked Anne to describe the ways in which her family had been affected by illness.

'Christopher was only 6 when I was first diagnosed, and so he wasn't really aware of what was going on. He's also a very happy-go-lucky little boy and so he's not the sort of child who worries.' Anne hesitated. 'But it really affected Jessie. She was 12 years old and she had a good idea of what was going on. Every time my temperature went up and I had to go into hospital, she got very upset. She used to cry a lot because she didn't think I was going to come back.' Anne smiled. 'After a few months, she realised that I always got better after a spell in hospital. Then she started asking questions and she began to understand a bit more about the leukaemia. Jessie liked to come up and visit me in hospital, but Christopher had had so much of hospitals that he wasn't keen to come. Sometimes he did come to see me, but he soon got bored and started running around the place, asking, "When can we go?" When John visited me, he used to leave Christopher with one of his friends; he was happy then.'

'What about the rest of the family? Were they able to come and see you?'

Anne nodded. 'My family came over from Somerset whenever they could. Then the doctors started talking about transplant, so there were all the tests on my family. I've got two sisters and a brother. One day, they all came over and we tramped down to the hospital together. There were lots of tests! A few weeks later, we got the results. They showed that my two sisters were both suitable. After that, they did two or three more tests, and they showed that they were both suitable all the way along.' Anne glanced at me and added, 'I could have had either one of them as a donor, which is quite unusual.'

'So you had a difficult choice to make,' I observed.

Anne nodded in agreement. 'Umm. Well, I couldn't decide, so I told them, "You'll have to decide between you." Anne shrugged her shoulders, conveying her vexation. 'They had a long chat together and decided between themselves. Age didn't really come into it. I'm the middle one. One of them is 2 years older than me and the other is 2 years younger. Now Geraldine, the older one, is married with two children, so they decided that my younger sister, Amy, who wasn't married at the time, would be the donor.... She must have been a good match because I've had no signs of rejection since the transplant.'

'When did you have the transplant?' I asked.

'July last year,' she replied. '13 months ago now.'

'How was the transplant?'

'Well, there's not a lot to say really. I wasn't worried about it. I just wanted to have it. I knew that if I didn't have it, I wouldn't get well.' She hesitated and glanced towards the door, apparently lost in her thoughts. 'I did get upset once,' she admitted.

'Tell me about that,' I encouraged.

'It was few weeks before I had the transplant. I went down to see Dr Green in the clinic. He told me about the transplant and all the things that could go wrong and that there was a possibility that I might not come out alive. I also went down to see the unit, and a couple of people had died there the previous day. Anyway, I was driving back home on my own and I had all these things going round in my head. I was really upset so I decided to call in and see Alan and Brenda. They're friends of ours from church and they live on the far side of town. By the time I got to their house, I was crying my eyes out. They took one look at me, took me inside, sat me down and gave me a cup of tea.' Anne's eyes glowed at the memory. 'We talked for a long time. Then we prayed together and I felt all right again. I was able to put it all out of my mind. After a day or two, I quite liked the idea of the transplant again.' Anne paused and looked at me with her steady grey eyes. 'Apart from that incident, I never really worried about the treatment. I didn't let any negative thoughts come into my mind.'

'Did you make a conscious decision not to think about all the things that could go wrong?' I asked.

'Well, I told you about the faith healing that I had before I went into the transplant.'

I nodded.

'I think I was slightly worried about it before that; but afterwards...'

'Can you tell me what happened at your faith healing?' I interjected.

Anne smiled. 'Yes. I was going to have my transplant in June, but for some reason, the doctors changed the date to July. I was worried because that was another month I had to wait, and I thought, "What's going to happen between now and then?" Anyway, they finally gave me the date, 23 July. It was the day of the royal wedding. Now I use a daily Bible reading guide called the *Daily Light*. When they gave me the date, something made me go and look it up in my *Daily Light*. The reading said, "Is any one of you sick? He should go to the elders of the church to pray over him and anoint him with oil in the name of the Lord. And the prayer offered in faith will make the sick person well; the Lord will raise him up." I thought, "Gosh, that's the second time I've been told to; I must go and ask for healing."'

Anne paused and then by way of explanation said, 'Just before I was ill, we had a speaker at church. He spoke about faith healing and said, "If you're ill, you must go and ask for healing yourself; no-one can do it for you. You must ask."' Anne paused again and then continued, 'When I read the passage in my *Daily Light*, I remembered his words and I realised that I had to do it. I'd been told to do it. So I went in to see one of the church elders, and I showed him the passage.'

'What did he say?' I asked.

'He said, "If that's what you want then yes, we will do it." He then explained that the elders had prayed once or twice with other people and they hadn't been healed. I said, "Oh, I know there's a chance that I might not be healed, but I feel that I must have this."' Anne paused and smiled. 'The elders arranged the date and John and I went up to the church. It was a Monday evening in July. It was a lovely, sunny evening and John and I went into the church. The elders were sat round the table at the front of the church. Anyway, I sat down in a chair and they all gathered round me and put their hands on me and prayed. Then one of them anointed me with oil. I could feel it on my skin. It was lovely.' Anne paused and smiled. 'I didn't feel anything immediately. I just felt comforted.... John and I came home and I went out into the garden, and suddenly, I felt completely different.'

'Can you describe how you felt?' I enquired

Anne furrowed her brows in concentration. 'It's difficult to describe, but I felt uplifted. I felt peaceful and contented. I felt marvellous. It was as though an enormous weight had been lifted off my shoulders, and I knew everything was going to be all right. I wasn't worried any more. In fact, I couldn't wait to get on with the transplant because I knew that I'd sail through it.'

'What about John? Did he feel any different.'

Anne shook her head. 'No. He didn't receive healing, like I did.... But he didn't seem worried. In fact, all the way through this, he's never appeared worried. At least, if he was, he didn't show it.'

'So then you went in for the transplant,' I prompted.

'Yes, then into the transplant. And there again,' she added, 'the church continued to pray for me while I was in having treatment. The day of the transplant, they had a day of prayer for me.'

Apparently, prior to her admission to the hospital, a prayer rota was pinned to the church notice board. Members of the church were then invited to sign their names, indicating a specific time when they would pray for Anne and her family. Essentially, they covered Anne with prayer.

'There was someone praying for me from morning till night. It was a marvellous thing to do and it really helped. I felt as though I was being carried along in their prayers.'

'So the transplant went well?' I suggested.

'Yes,' she affirmed. 'I just sailed through it. I didn't have any problems while I was in.'

'No problems with the chemotherapy and radiotherapy?'

'No problems,' she repeated and then, as an afterthought, added, 'Well, the chemotherapy wasn't very nice. I was very sick after that. But the radiotherapy wasn't bad. Although I had pains in my legs and I couldn't keep still, it wasn't too bad. It took about 3 hours to complete.... They gave me some Valium, but it didn't take effect for ages.' Anne chuckled. 'I was wide awake until the last hour when I got dozy and eventually drifted off to sleep. When the treatment was finished, I went back to the General, had another course of chemo and then had the transplant overnight. After that, I was in for about 3 weeks, and I must say I got bored at times.'

'You got bored,' I repeated.

Anne gave a nod of agreement. 'Yes, the mornings were all right. After breakfast, I was busy with doctors' visits, blood tests, cleaning the Hickman line and so on. Then I'd have a long wash and so time went quite quickly. But I found that the afternoons dragged a bit.'

'Were you not able to read and things?' I asked.

'Yes, I wrote letters and did some embroidery. I also received lots of cards and letters every day, which was nice, so I read them and then watched television.' Anne grimaced. 'Oh, I did watch television. They had a video machine, so I watched videos. When I came out, I thought I'd never watch television again!' Anne laughed and added, 'The nurses were very kind, though. They used to come in and chat to me and I used to help them make the bed.'

'It sounds as though you were looking for things to do,' I observed.

Anne nodded. 'I was.' Then, becoming more serious she said, 'It was those quiet times that made me realise how I missed my freedom, how I missed being able to go out to a friends for a cup of coffee, how I missed being able to go out into the garden and pull up a few weeds.' She chuckled and admitted, 'I even missed doing the housework...! But it was nice when I came home and was able to mix with people again, when I could invite people round for coffee, go out to the shops and have a kiss from the children.' She paused and then continued describing her impressions of the unit. 'The food wasn't very appetising either.'

'Yes, all the tinned food must be awful,' I sympathised.

'It wasn't very pleasant,' she confessed. 'I could still taste it then. Later, after I came home, I lost my sense of taste completely. There were so many things that I couldn't eat. Everything had a peculiar taste, unless it was very bland. Even now, I'm still not back to normal. There are still some things I can't eat, like highly spiced or highly flavoured foods.' Anne sat in silence for a few moments. 'One thing I particularly used to enjoy was chocolate. I can't stand it now. I can't even stand the smell of it. In fact, if I do eat it, I feel really sick.' She gave a wry smile. 'I don't think I'll ever eat curry again either. I had one while I was on the transplant unit. It was a couple of weeks after the transplant and there was curry on the menu. I thought, "Oh, that would be nice. I'll try it."' Anne pulled a face and said, 'I was ill all night!' She laughed. 'Anyway, I'm enjoying my food now. It took me a long time to get back to eating normally, and I lost quite a lot of weight....'

'Did you worry about your weight while you were ill?' I enquired.

'Yes,' she conceded, 'I did. I couldn't eat very much at the beginning. In fact, I had to force myself to eat enough to keep going. After about 6 months, my appetite gradually came back and I was able to eat normally, and slowly I started to put weight on again....' She paused and added as an afterthought, 'I had difficulty sleeping, as well.'

'You had problems sleeping?'

Anne nodded. 'It started on the transplant unit. It was so noisy in the room off Intensive Care, I had to take sleeping tablets. I got used to taking them and so, when I got home, I couldn't sleep without them.... I had to take sleeping tablets for quite a long time.' Anne glanced at me quickly. 'I used to get them from my GP and he never questioned me, so I thought, "Well it's all right." Anyway, someone else found out I was having them and they told me to stop taking them. I was taking two a night, so I cut down to one a night and I got a few hours sleep. But if I didn't take one, I didn't get any sleep at all. I literally felt ill without them. Gradually, I managed to take a night here and there without them, and then I only took them when I really needed them.

So eventually, I managed to wean myself off them.' Anne gave a shy smile.

I complimented Anne. 'You did well. It's not easy to come off them.' Then, seeking to steer the conversation back to the transplant and the period of isolation, I asked, 'Did you mind being in a single room on your own?'

Anne shrugged her shoulders to convey her indifference. 'Well, I got used to it, and it wasn't too bad. John used to come and see me every day, and people used to come to the doorway and I could talk to them on my little walkie-talkie thing. But it was daunting coming home after 3 weeks in that room... Everything was so spotless in there. The air was clean. Everything I ate was clean. Everything was new, and nothing had germs on it; even the soap was changed every day. Coming out into the big wide world which was full of germs, I thought, "Gosh, how am I going to survive?"'

'It must have been very frightening,' I remarked.

Anne nodded. 'It was. I thought, "How am I going to avoid getting an infection?"'

'And how did you avoid catching anything?' I asked.

'Well, I didn't go out visiting people. They used to visit me instead, and they all knew to stay away if they had a cold or anything like that. My brother and sister came over now and again, and my mother came to stay for a while to help.' Anne paused and explained, 'I wasn't very strong when I came home. I didn't have any muscles left and I looked really skinny.' She grinned and confessed, 'I should've done more exercises while I was in.... When I came out I had a lot of visitors from church. They organised a visiting rota for me. People took it in turns to come and visit me. Some people just sat and chatted with me, while others did some housework or shopping for me. One or two people even came round to tidy the garden, which was nice....'

The support provided by Anne's church family was vital to her recovery. Support in the form of practical help, emotional solace and spiritual aid strengthened Anne and freed her to fight illness. Nevertheless, despite the remarkable support provided by her church family, I wondered if Anne had experienced periods of doubt and depression. Had she questioned her faith during her illness? Anne renounced my assumption vehemently.

'No, I never blamed God or anything like that. At one time, I did think, "Why has this happened to me? Why not somebody else?" But then I remember thinking, "It's not right to think like that. There must be a reason for it."' She paused and then added, 'In fact, it has made my faith stronger. Before this happened, I never did much with my faith. I went to church once a week and to Bible study, but not much else. But this has made me realise how precious life is, and it's made me realise that I should be doing more with my faith....'

The telephone rang, its shrill tone interrupting our discussion. After a short conversation, Anne resumed her train of thought.

'It's made a difference to our church as well.'

'In what ways?' I asked.

Anne paused. 'Well, they seem to be a lot closer. In the last couple of years, a lot of people in the church have been ill and there's been a lot of prayer, and this prayer has brought us closer together.' Anne smiled and added, as an afterthought, 'It's my family.... In fact,' she admitted, 'I'm a lot closer to some of the people at church than I am to my own parents. Well, the people at church have gone through the illness with me and I've shared things with them that I couldn't share with my own family. I've got one special friend called Grace. I can tell her perhaps more than I can my own mother. Well, my mother is such a worrier and so I can never tell her anything. If I'm on the phone to her and she thinks there's something wrong, she'll fret and worry, so I don't tell her things. I'll tell one of my friends instead....'

Now, 2 years since her diagnosis, I wondered what the long-term effects of Anne's illness had been. Had relationships within her family altered?

'John and I are closer together. With Christopher, I don't know if things have changed or not. He's always been happy-go-lucky and affectionate. He'll come up to me and put his arms around me and hug me.' She paused and added with a grin, 'He wouldn't do it in front of his friends, mind you! Now, Jessie's completely different. She was very upset when I was diagnosed. Then, when I was having the transplant, she went away for a while to a friend's house. But she didn't like being away, so she came home and looked after herself.' Anne glanced at me and explained, 'John was out at work during the day, so she grew up very quickly.'

'She sounds very independent,' I observed.

'Yes, she is.' Anne agreed. 'When she comes in, she gets her own meals. This is almost a bed-and-breakfast for her.'

'Does she talk about the past at all?' I asked.

'Sometimes she does, yes. But she doesn't worry about me now like she used to. I suppose she thinks, "God's healed Mummy. She's all right and I needn't worry about her any more."'

Instead of pursuing the topic further, I asked Anne whether she had changed as a result of illness. 'What about you, Anne? Has the illness changed you?'

She sat thinking about my question for a few moments and then replied, 'Yes, I think I have. I think I'm a better person for what has happened.'

'In what way?' I encouraged.

'Well, I'm a much calmer person now. I'm more contented. Before I was ill, I used to want things. I wanted a bigger house and a bigger car. Now I don't want to move and I don't feel that I want anything. I've got everything I need: I've got a lovely family, enough money to live on, lovely friends, my faith. What more could I want?'

'Priorities change, don't they?' I remarked.

'Yes,' Anne assented.

'What are your thoughts for the future?'

Anne shrugged her shoulders. 'Oh, I don't plan ahead. I don't plan next year's holiday or anything.' She frowned and tried to clarify her argument. 'I suppose I plan what we're going to do the next month, but I don't plan any further ahead than that.'

'Did you plan before you were ill?'

Anne laughed and confessed, 'I don't know whether I did before all this happened. But while I was ill, I certainly didn't! Then it was one day at a time. I didn't want to know too much either. I didn't want to know what was going to happen the next week. I just wanted to know what was happening now.' Anne stared at the empty mug that lay in her lap. 'I don't know whether the chemotherapy made my brain go a bit funny, a bit slow, but I couldn't remember things after a while.

I used to forget things. I'd be out in the car for instance, and I couldn't think where I was going. After a while, it would come back to me, but my brain just seemed very slow.'

'Has your memory improved now?'

'Yes, it has improved.' Anne acknowledged. 'When I came out of the transplant unit my brain was very slow. I couldn't concentrate to read. I could pick up a magazine and skim through it, but I couldn't read a book.'

'Did that worry you?' I interposed.

'I wouldn't say it worried me, particularly.' Anne explained. 'I just thought, "Well, it's been shut away for so long, it must be that."'

At that point, Christopher arrived home from school. He came into the room, threw himself into a chair and stared at me. A few minutes later, having convinced himself that I wasn't very interesting, he announced that he was going outside to play football with his friends. Anne smiled happily as the small figure disappeared out of the room. Realising that Anne would have to start preparing supper for her family, I tried to bring the conversation to a close.

'Have you had any doubts since you've had the transplant?'

Anne shook her head. 'Not when I'm feeling well,' she said. 'But I do get ups and downs. A couple of weeks ago, I had a high temperature and I thought, "Gosh, am I going to be able to fight this thing off?"' She paused and added, 'I suppose I wouldn't be human if I didn't doubt now and again, but on the whole, I don't worry about it. I don't sit around wondering what's going to happen next year or anything like that. But if I get ill, I do worry a bit.'

'You worry a little bit.' I repeated Anne's words.

'Well, I worry about what it is. I worry about my family. While I was ill, I didn't know if I was going to get better. A lot of people on the ward died from leukaemia and I knew I could be one of them. At the same time, I wasn't frightened of dying, because I knew that if I died, my life wouldn't end there.... But I was worried about leaving my family behind. I wondered who would look after them and how they would manage.... I still worry even now. But whenever I start worrying, I hear this voice saying, "I did my healing on that night." Then it comes back to me. I remember the elders praying for me and

9. ANNE

I remember the feeling I had in the garden, and I think, "What am I worrying about?" My worries just disappear and I know everything is going to be all right.'

Postscript

In September 1992 I received a letter from Anne bringing me up to date with her medical condition and her home life. In the letter, she wrote:

> *It is now 6 years since my bone marrow transplant, and I have been very well during this time. The radiotherapy treatment caused me to have cataracts and I have had two successful operations of lens implants. It is wonderful to be able to see clearly again....*

Anne went on to describe how over the last couple of years she had done some temporary clerical work and was now applying for a part-time secretarial job. She also reported that she had taken up painting as a hobby and had recently sold several of her paintings, raising money for charity.

*   *   *   *   *

10. *Discussion and conclusions*

THE PURPOSE OF THIS BOOK WAS TO EXPLORE AND DESCRIBE THE LIVED experience and meaning of leukaemia by describing illness from the patients' perspective. The intention was to gain a valid and authentic understanding of the illness process and to uncover its potential for personal growth and development. This chapter presents a discussion of the personal accounts and explores the issues arising from them.

The chapter is divided into four sections. Section I explores the impact of illness, and looks at the implications for nursing practice. Section II presents a discussion of the research interview and the ethical issues involved in research. Section III examines the limitations of the book and offers some suggestions for future work. Finally, Section IV considers the implications for nursing education.

Section I: The impact and meaning of illness

The personal accounts illustrate the uniqueness of the individual's experience of illness. They also identify the commonalities of the disease process by the presence of prevalent patterns and themes. In particular, all the participants endured the multiple losses that accompany diagnosis with a life-threatening disease. They bore the physical changes associated with the disease process and the side-effects of aggressive chemotherapy that resulted in the loss of their body image. They suffered the forced dependence on professional staff, treatment modalities, family and friends that led to the loss of their independence and autonomy, and they tolerated prolonged periods of hospitalisation that caused isolation and separation leading to the loss of their social image. Finally, the uncertainty of living with a life-threatening illness affected their future and challenged their personal beliefs. Essentially, all the participants faced a total depersonalisation, a loss of their identity.

The loss of identity evoked a strong emotional and behavioural response. Endeavouring to come to terms with illness and grieve for their losses, the participants detached themselves from the normal world and confronted the leukaemia in the way that they knew best. Leukaemia then became a way of life. Gradually the participants learned the skills and adopted the lifestyle of a leukaemic patient, balancing their needs as both a patient and a person. With the goals of remission, cure and recovery, they did everything possible to control and defeat the disease.

Transplant was a transition point in the participants' career as leukaemics. It marked the climax of their recovery. It was also a time of renewed dependency and uncertainty. If successful, the participants could return to normal life; however, if it failed or their disease relapsed, they faced the resumption of chemotherapy and further illness and potential death.

In contrast to the intensive physical and emotional preparation for transplant, the procedure itself was comparatively uneventful, a simple transfusion. Then came the boredom of isolation, a period of passive getting well, waiting to see if the graft had taken. Once again, the participants' goal was simply to control the disease. Providing the transplant progressed smoothly, they then entered the final stage of illness, the return to normal life. This involved a shedding of the patient identity and re-entry into the normal world. It was a period of readjustment and rebuilding.

Unfortunately, if the transplant failed or the leukaemia relapsed, the participants experienced renewed personal losses and returned to a life of uncertainty. In restaging the fight against leukaemia, they sought to confront and control the disease once again. In the event of treatment failure, the participants then entered the terminal phase of illness. In this end phase, they acknowledged their defeat and finally gave up the struggle for survival, submitting themselves to illness and death.

Implications for nursing practice

In the vignette accounts, it is apparent that many patients struggle with the loss of control following their diagnosis and the commencement of chemotherapy. This loss of control is all consuming and creates within the individual feelings of fear, anxiety, depression,

10. DISCUSSION AND CONCLUSIONS

guilt, hopelessness, loneliness and confusion. In order to help, nurses and other care-givers must endeavour to empower the person, thereby restoring an element of control to his life.

In practical terms, this empowering encompasses symptom relief, emotional support, the promotion of autonomy and independence through education, encouragement and counselling, and the provision of supportive relationships.

Symptom relief

Symptoms are never simple to the leukaemic patient. A bruise represents a low platelet count and may signify the failure of treatment and the relapse of the disease. Other symptoms, such as nausea and vomiting, diarrhoea, anorexia and weight loss, dyspnoea, pain and insomnia, cause physical and emotional distress; they may also represent an inability to control the disease itself.

The relief of demoralising symptoms brings physical comfort and re-establishes hope as the individual's sense of control is restored. Moreover, the person experiences a growing trust and confidence in the care-givers as symptoms are treated successfully. Similarly, practical intervention such as the provision of a wig, turban or headscarf for alopecia enhances a person's self-esteem by helping to restore his identity (please note, the physical 'cover up' does not eradicate the need for appropriate emotional support). Even in terminal illness, the relief of distressing symptoms can establish a measure of personal control and can enhance the quality of remaining life.

The use of self-help techniques is known to magnify the patient's sense of control over illness (Simonton et al 1978). Certainly, several participants described how they adopted methods of relaxation, visualisation, breathing exercises, imagery and massage in order to counter and control their symptoms. If their symptoms diminished or their coping methods were successful, the participants were elated. They had power; they had achieved a personal victory over the illness. From these observations, it is clearly important for nurses to encourage and facilitate the use of self-help techniques in patients that wish to use them. However, it is also critical that staff do not coerce a patient to use techniques that he is either unwilling or unable to implement.

10. DISCUSSION AND CONCLUSIONS

Emotional support

During illness, the patient's emotions are dynamic and labile. Physical ill-health, the psychological pressures of living with a life-threatening illness and ever-changing personal circumstances contribute to the person's rapid mood swings and emotional distress. The harmful emotions of depression, anxiety, anger, guilt, resentment and grief are a barrier to physical healing and psychological well-being. Consequently, there is a need for psychological assessment (Snyder & Wilson 1977) and patients then need help to identify, work through and express their emotional pain.

The personal accounts identify the need to involve patients in care. Active participation helps patients to overcome the fear, anxiety and depression associated with illness. The involvement in practical aspects of care, the act of learning to master a simple skill and taking responsibility for an aspect of care, consumes their time, attention and energy. They are unable to think about themselves and worry.

Humour is a useful tool in relieving painful emotions and promoting health. The participants used humour to relieve stress and to overcome depression. Humour allowed them to 'escape from reality'; it made them 'feel better'. Often, during outpatient appointments, the participants would get together and have a laugh and joke. These findings, supported by the literature (Bellert 1989, Cousins 1979, Herth 1990), indicate that humour can be used to promote healing in patients with leukaemia. Therefore, it is important that professional staff introduce and encourage the use of humour in the therapeutic environment. For instance, Rowden (1984) suggests that the staff may instil humour into the illness experience by using comedy tapes and videos on the ward.

In life-threatening illness, it is important to verify with the patients what they actually fear and then to provide them with appropriate support that will help them to cope with these fears. For instance, leukaemic patients may be concerned about illness and whether they will be able to cope with the tests and treatment modalities; they may be anxious about their families and what will happen at home, or they may be fearful of death itself. Each of these concerns needs to be addressed.

The leukaemic patient also has several unique illness concerns. In order to identify these, the nurse must listen to and work with the patient. Firstly, it is important to verify with the person what he actually expects from care, and secondly, what he needs from care. Thirdly, it is vital to ascertain a person's likes and dislikes so that care is appropriate and the patient complies with his treatment and is happy.

Bill's account demonstrates what happens when staff fail to listen to a patient. Bill told the staff that he didn't like Caloreen (a high-calorie powder that can be added to food and beverages). Unfortunately, the staff kept adding Caloreen to his drinks without consulting him. They were then surprised when he became belligerent and refused to drink the 'stuff.' Conversely, Bill perceived their action as discourteous and disrespectful.

Autonomy and independence

The professional system often dictates the how and why of treatment, while patients' input into the medical, nursing and hospital routines and policies is minimal. The vignettes demonstrate that patients are experts. Additionally, they show that most patients wish to be independent if and when their condition allows for autonomy. Consequently, it is important that patients be given a role in defining their needs and desires with regard to the administration of treatment, and that they be allowed to assume a greater level of independence in their activities of daily living. In this way, patients are able to realise a measure of self-respect and can live through the illness passage in a more meaningful way.

Personal control was a major theme in the personal accounts. This indicates the importance of encouraging and equipping patients to adopt active and appropriate coping strategies. Even in acute illness, patients can still maintain a level of control, providing that their expectations are flexible and realistic.

Unfortunately, some individuals adopt maladaptive or non-effective coping techniques. Coping behaviour is deemed ineffective when it prevents the patient from selecting treatment or when it interferes with his treatment. Another sign of ineffective coping behaviour is that the patient forsakes everyday normal function.

Mental defence strategies initially serve a protective function but, on a long-term basis, they prevent the person from coming to terms with illness and can be harmful. In this situation, the individual can be encouraged to change and use a more active coping style. However, before staff challenge a person's passive defence mechanisms, they must ensure that he has an alternative and appropriate means of support.

Staff members sometimes fail to interpret a patient's defence strategies. Ron, for example, was unable to cope with the death of his colleagues and friends and so he adopted a simple denial response. During his visits to the ward he deliberately avoided asking about the other patients. Sadly, however, the staff always told him when one of his friends had died. Each time, he was shattered by the news.

Education

Knowledge is a key resource for leukaemic patients. It helps them to overcome the shock of diagnosis and it counteracts their fear of the unknown. Knowledge enables them to participate in care and allows them to gain a measure of control over illness. There is also evidence to show that information aids compliance with treatment regimes (Holland 1977).

The pen portraits illuminate the changing pattern of the participants' information needs. The participants wanted information in stages and they sought information in accordance with their ability to cope. Initially, they required a basic description of the disease process, the tests and the treatment regimes. They wanted to know the side-effects of the chemotherapy and the effects of the illness on their normal lives. Essentially, they also wanted hope; they wanted to know that there was treatment available.

Once the shock of diagnosis had begun to diminish, the patients were instructed in simple skills, such as temperature recording, skin checks and mouth care techniques. These skills helped them to avoid injury and infection and allowed them a greater level of self-care. Gradually, as the illness progressed and their understanding developed, they received more formal teaching. This teaching focussed on problem-solving and the acquisition of skilled tasks, for example the care of the Hickman line and knowledge about nutrition and diet. The patients were also kept informed of changes in their treatment and of their ongoing test results.

After relapse or the failure of treatment, the participants experienced a loss of faith: their morale collapsed. Afraid that 'nothing more could be done', they questioned the staff constantly. They demanded information on the disease process, the test results and the treatments available. Information became a lifeline for them.

Various factors were seen to inhibit the patient's ability to learn and assimilate factual information. Physical debility and acute illness caused memory loss and an inability to concentrate, while emotional distress (anxiety, depression and grief) initiated the development of defence mechanisms such as denial and learned helplessness and caused further learning setbacks.

In order to counteract these problems, it is important that information be given in simple terms that the patient can understand. Instructions should be repeated in order to overcome memory loss, while frequent questioning enables the patient's level of comprehension to be assessed. It is also vital that teaching be done at an appropriate time. Periods when patients are acutely ill, for example, are entirely inappropriate for teaching. Not only are the patients too ill to listen, concentrate and learn but, more importantly, they are too ill to care.

The use of visual aids is beneficial to the learning process. When Anne was first diagnosed, she wanted to know all about her disease. In order to explain the pathology of leukaemia, the doctor took her to the hospital laboratory and showed her slides of normal and leukaemic blood cells under the microscope. Seeing the cells helped her to understand her disease. Similarly, whenever Richard questioned the doctors about his illness or an aspect of treatment, he asked them to draw pictures as this helped him to understand. Finally, the use of videos and films that portray the patient's experience of illness are often beneficial.

The provision of written material is also helpful to learning. A leaflet or booklet describing a clinical technique and the associate 'do's' and 'don'ts' of procedures such as bone marrow aspiration (O'Rourke 1986), bone marrow harvest (Holcombe 1987), bone marrow transplant (Almquist et al 1986) or care of the Hickman line (Howser 1987) gives patients a good insight and understanding of the experience and enables them to identify their role. In addition, written material also overcomes the problem of memory loss.

Inadequate patient teaching and poor communication result in ignorance and helplessness. They also lead to misunderstanding between the nurse and patient, causing a breakdown in their relationship. Due to poor communication and lack of teaching, Bill was unable to come to terms with his treatment and care. Without clinical understanding, he turned instead to his own past experiences and common sense. He rebelled against the professional staff, failing to comply with some of the clinical demands they imposed.

In retrospect, it is easy to recognise Bill's need for teaching. Periodically during his illness, he needed a nurse or doctor to sit down with him and give him a detailed explanation of his treatment and care. He needed time to ask questions and to have the facts repeated and clarified. He needed time to reflect on the information and the things he had learnt. Perhaps he would also have benefited from a joint teaching session with his wife.

Medical jargon was a further source of confusion among the participants. Initially, they were confused and alienated by hospital jargon. However, they soon learnt to translate the technical language and could comprehend the complex clinical slang or 'hospitalese.' Gradually, they began to use jargon themselves, integrating words into their own vocabulary. Richard described how mastery of clinical jargon allowed him to 'communicate with the doctors on level terms'. Ironically, this ability to converse freely represented equality with the professionals and gave him a sense of autonomy and worth.

Instilling hope

Patients need hope throughout the illness passage. Hope is vital to their morale. Cousins (1982, p.588) describes how professionals need to convey information in a way that 'is received by the patient as a challenge rather than a death sentence'. Essentially, knowledge must be tempered with hope.

In the accounts, two participants described how they were devastated by the news of their diagnoses. The doctors didn't know how to tell them; they broke the news bluntly and without compassion. Several other participants remarked that they needed information at the time of their diagnosis, but not too much. They needed to know that there was treatment available and that they had the goal of remission to aim for. They also needed to hear that they had an important role in treatment, that they could contribute to their own recovery. Then, during the treatment, they needed to know what was happening and what the future plans were. They needed to know the truth, and they could accept bad news when it was tempered with hope. In contrast, the participants described how they did not need to know the gruesome details of illness. The following extract captures these sentiments:

> *I'd prefer them not to say, 'You're going to have such a bad throat that you won't be able to swallow.' No! But I'd like them to say, 'You'll have a problem with your throat, but we're here to help you get over it. It won't last long, and you'll get better.' (Dave)*

Conversely, artificial optimism and false hope merely separated the participants from their care-givers. This contradiction of existence increased their sense of alienation and isolation, generating feelings of anxiety and anguish.

It is important to note that some patients are unable to handle the truth even when there is hope. For instance, during episodes of acute illness, several participants commented that they didn't want to know how ill they were. 'Blissful ignorance' was the only thing that counteracted their anxiety and enabled them to retain a sense of hope. Alan, for instance, was critically ill with haematuria during his transplant. Instead of telling him that he was dying of uncontrollable bleeding, the staff said, 'There's nothing to worry about.' Alan was able to cope. After his discharge, his mother told him that he had nearly died. At that point in his recovery, the knowledge gave him a sense of satisfaction; he felt that he had beaten the leukaemia.

The accounts demonstrate how leukaemic patients often compare themselves with other leukaemic patients. They find it stimulating and encouraging to hear about fellow patients who have recovered or are doing well. It is, therefore, important that people who are responding well to treatment or who have been 'cured' go back on to the wards to talk with and encourage the newly diagnosed patients and those who are struggling through treatment. As Dave said 'to show them that there is light at the end of the tunnel'.

If no patients are available, biographical accounts, newspaper articles and video recordings of people who have conquered their disease are also helpful. One woman recounted how a newspaper report had encouraged her:

The best thing on the ward when we were there was a picture of a girl from Dinas Powys. She had had a transplant. It was a newspaper article, just pinned to the wall.... (Mary)

Sadly, some patients do not respond to treatment. When a patient has relapsed or died, it is necessary for the staff to counteract the 'bad news' by reassuring other patients that they are not in the same situation. For instance, the staff can emphasise differences in the disease process, the treatment regimes and the person himself.

Finally, when cure is no longer possible, it is important that care retains an element of hope. Instead of the hope of cure, there remains the hope of comfort and continued help. This hope helps to offset the fear of abandonment and isolation.

The power of words

Professional staff influence the patient's state of mind through the words they speak. Cousins writes how their words have the power to encourage or devastate. 'Words used by physicians and nurses have a profound effect on the well-being of the patient. They can open the way to recovery, or they can make a patient dependent, tremulous, fearful or resistant.' (Cousins 1982, p.257.)

In general, the participants echoed these sentiments. Constantly looking for clues to assess their condition, they would cling to every word spoken by a staff member. They analysed and compared each verbal and non-verbal report. Indeed, non-verbal cues often had more impact than the spoken word. Facial expression, eye contact, the tone of voice were all appraised. They had the capacity to inspire confidence and hope or to impart anxiety and confusion. Waiting for news of her bone marrow transplant, one patient reported that she was alert to her doctor's every expression: 'I could tell by his eyes that it was good news....' (Mary). Accordingly, when a member of staff made an off-hand remark, it had a devastating effect on the patient. Moreover, when staff used hackneyed phrases, common platitudes or simply failed to listen, it represented a lack of concern and a sign of disrespect.

Setting goals

Throughout the illness passage, realistic goal setting gave the participants a sense of purpose and meaning. The achievement of these goals gave them hope and encouragement and enabled them to maintain a measure of personal control. The participants set themselves short- and long-term goals. Short-term goals served to motivate them to overcome the immediate problems of illness. For instance, one young man enjoyed watching the weekly episode of the television detective programme *Bergerac*. His determination to see the programme enabled him to endure the discomfort of a severe nosebleed. In contrast, long-term goals gave the participants something to look forward to, allowing them to escape from the 'tunnel vision' of illness. In between her courses of chemotherapy, Dorothy's family arranged special family times for her. During her treatment, Dorothy was able to focus her thoughts on these gatherings and could escape from the unpleasantness of her situation.

In leukaemia, the illness passage is signposted by medical goals of treatment. When treatment is progressing well, individuals adopt these goals and monitor their progress according to them. However, when treatment fails and relapse occurs, individuals may reject medical goals and decide to discontinue treatment. Under these circumstances, it is important that the professional staff respect patients' wishes, allowing them to 'let go'. This support sustains the patients' confidence in the staff and allows them to have a peace of mind.

Staff–patient relationships: the therapeutic partnership

According to the participants, their relationship with individual members of staff was a key factor in determining their ability to cope with illness. The relationships helped them to overcome their feelings of alienation and isolation and aided their adjustment to the illness. The participants depended on the staff for clinical expertise and knowledge and for reassurance, empathy and encouragement. The need for staff support varied from person to person and the individual's need fluctuated during the course of his illness.

The participants carefully appraised each member of the staff before they formed a relationship with any one of them. Some developed a friendship with a particular nurse, while others chose a physician. Dr Roberts, for instance, was a vital resource for Dorothy. He represented security, creating a healing environment for her; his presence was as important to her as the treatment itself. In contrast, Dr Green generated a sense of awe and fear in her; she was frightened to ask him questions. Interestingly, however, when Dorothy was ill on the transplant unit she found that Dr Green was very supportive. He was 'a great comfort' to her and 'a great source of strength'.

First encounters with the staff were particularly important when it came to forming relationships. One participant commented:

> When I first came on the ward, before I'd been told that I had leukaemia, Sister Jones was there, and she shook my hand. I had two reactions to this. I thought, 'Oh this is marvellous, I've never had this before!' And I thought, 'Why is she treating me like this?' But on thinking about it, I realised that this sort of attitude is all sort of part and parcel of the treatment, and it definitely does help a lot. The initial period when I was in for 6 weeks, I found the attitude of the nursing staff – not so much the medical staff, the nursing staff – was such that it made me feel better about everything.... (Dave)

Each time they started a new phase of treatment or entered a new therapeutic environment, the participants became fearful and apprehensive. On these occasions, personal contact with a member of staff was vital and the participants found it particularly helpful if they knew the person who was treating them.

Illness with leukaemia strips the person of his physical appearance, social image and self-esteem. He is left feeling abnormal and isolated. Human contact helps to reinforce the person's hold on reality. It helps the person regain his individuality. One patient described how she sometimes just needed company: she needed a nurse to come in and chat, not do anything, just chat. Similarly, there were occasions when another patient needed the nurses to come in and say 'Hello!' or 'Good morning.' He needed a 'human comment' to make him feel normal, instead of 'some sort of freak in a glass cage'.

Finally, the participants also needed to have their contribution to care recognised, their opinions listened to and their time honoured. They needed to feel that they were special to the staff and that whether they lived or died was important. They needed to feel accepted, trusted, respected and loved. A nurse–patient relationship based on these qualities instils a sense of meaning and purpose into the illness process and helps to restore the patient's sense of identity.

The need for counselling – 'talking helps'

Illness clearly challenges and affects people in all aspects of life. In order to accept the new patient identity and realise a sense of purpose and meaning in the illness experience, patients need to talk through many things, from simple practical issues to complex emotional and spiritual concerns (Travelbee 1971). Even if questions and problems remain unresolved, the act of sharing may relieve the individual's inner tension, his fear of isolation. Sharing becomes particularly important in the solitude of terminal illness when a person is struggling to accept his own mortality.

The accounts of illness confirm that people who have been diagnosed with life-threatening disease do need counselling. They need to talk and to be understood. Unable to converse with family members who were struggling to come to terms with the illness, several participants commented that they would have benefited from professional counselling. Unhappily, they also described how the nurses and other professionals failed to recognise their need for counselling and 'never had time to talk'. Consequently, although a few were counselled by the staff, most of the participants turned to friends and relatives for help. Some struggled through illness alone.

Counselling in illness needs to be dynamic. In the early stages, patients are often 'too shocked to talk.' But then, as the numbness wears off, the need to talk increases; they need to 'talk the stress out'. One man recalled how his need for counselling varied as his illness progressed. 'My need to talk would vary. Sometimes I wanted to talk and at other times I just wanted to forget.'

Watson (1990) describes how the patient's need to talk also continues into the recovery period. Accordingly, the participants' need for counselling often increased as they struggled to reintegrate into the normal world, trying to reconcile their new beliefs and values with a suitable career and seeking to realise a new identity. Richard described the patient's plight as follows:

> *A lot of people who have survived cancer or serious threats to their lives have gone through so much that they're confused. They're not sure why*

they survived and they're not sure what to do next. Should they go back into the routine again which they're going to find completely unsatisfactory, or should they find something more meaningful?

He went on to suggest:

I think counselling is important for people who've survived their illness, to direct them and help them use the experience instead of losing it completely....'

Burnard (1989) describes how counselling or the 'therapeutic conversation' may be used to explore the patient's perception of his situation and facilitate his adaptation to illness. In hospital, the periods of staff–patient interaction provide both an opportunity and a context conducive to the discussion of personal issues. In the recovery period, the patient's general status can be assessed during an outpatient appointment. If a person has severe emotional or psychological problems that cannot be addressed during the time of the appointment, a consultation for further counselling or psychotherapy may be arranged.

Family support

From the vignette accounts it is clear that illness impacts heavily upon the spouse and other family members of the leukaemic patient. In addition to the practical concerns of family life, such as altered roles and family structure, the family have to bear the heavy emotional burdens of illness. They have to come to terms with the infirmity and potential death of the patient. Therefore, it is important that the staff are aware of the need to provide the family with adequate support.

The marital partner is essential to the patient's self-esteem and his ability to cope with illness. Moreover, the spouse often shoulders many of the illness burdens and therefore requires particular support throughout the illness passage. Watson (1982) cites the value of educating the spouse so that he can participate in care. This involvement allows the spouse to feel that he has an important role to play in the patient's recovery; it allows him to feel useful. Certainly, Dorothy's husband, Tom, benefited from the teaching he received, and he appreciated being included in Dorothy's care. Stedeford (1983) purports that counselling can enhance the spouse's ability to cope with illness, enabling him to accompany the patient throughout illness. Furthermore, she writes that counselling sessions may forge communication links between the family members, enriching family relationships.

As patients witness the pain their family members endure during illness, they often try to protect and shield their family from the stresses of illness. Children pose a particular problem, as patients are often uncertain how much to tell them or how much to show them. Secrecy and concealment generate fear, particularly in children. Consequently, it is important that patients are taught and encouraged to expose their illness to members of the family. If children are introduced to illness in a gentle and non-threatening manner, they will not reject the ill parent. One patient, Gerry, wouldn't allow her 4-year-old daughter, Jenny, to see her while she was ill. She thought Jenny would be frightened and upset if she saw her mummy so ill. Later, however, when Jenny did see her mum, she coped well. Even Gerry's alopecia didn't disturb her. Following this experience, Gerry had the confidence to explain her illness to Jenny, using simple terminology and humour.

Section II: A critique of the data collection

This section will address issues arising from the data collection. First, the formal interview and written brief are examined and second, the ethical problems that emerged during the study are discussed.

The formal interview

The formal interview was the major means of data collection. Although this method was entirely appropriate to the study, various problems were encountered during the interviews, including stage fright, environmental stress and infirmity, role conflict and poor interviewing technique.

Stage fright is a common pitfall in the research interview, particularly when a tape-recorder is used (Field & Morse 1985). Certainly, two of the participants felt self-conscious and inhibited by the tape-recorder. However, as they became involved in conversation, they forgot their embarrassment. Consequently, in order to establish contact with the participants and to overcome their nervousness, I began each interview by asking the person to talk about his illness or to describe a recent life experience.

201

Environmental stress was not a major problem as most interviews were performed in the relaxed atmosphere of the patient's own home or in the quiet surroundings of the ward office. In contrast, however, the clinic, with its inherent tension of medical consultations and impending test results, generated much anxiety. Furthermore, due to the limited number of rooms available and the busy clinic schedule, the interviews were often interrupted. In hindsight, it would have been helpful to hang a 'Do Not Disturb' notice on the door and to disconnect the telephone during the interview sessions.

The participants' interview performance was inevitably impaired during periods of acute illness. The aggressive chemotherapy and radiotherapy caused memory loss and physical infirmity, while the emotional and psychological stresses of illness served to colour their perceptions of illness, influencing the interview material. Nevertheless, the content of these interviews describes and explores an integral part of illness and it therefore explains an important facet of the whole illness experience.

'Role conflict' is a known problem in nursing research (Aamodt 1986). Certainly, I experienced difficulty with my combined status of nurse, researcher and friend. For example, several participants sought clinical advice during the interviews, while others chose to discuss their fellow patients. In addition, I was the subject of role confusion. When participants were hospitalised, I sometimes visited them informally. On these occasions, several relatives mistook me for the ward social worker as I was dressed in civilian clothes.

Field & Morse (1985) discuss the many elements of poor interviewing and describe how poor interviewing habits such as bombardment, advice-giving, double-blind questioning and using cliches serve to block and limit the data collection. During the course of data collection, I became aware of the limitations in my own interviewing technique. The initial interviews were hurried, 'cues' were overlooked and conversation was shallow and disjointed. Gradually, however, I acquired the skills of exploration and active listening. I learnt how to expose the participants' emotions and feelings and how to reflect their comments in order to validate my interpretation of their experiences. Fortunately, my willingness to accompany the participants through illness and my concern for them overcame the negative effect of my inadequate interviewing technique. As relationships developed, the participants shared their experiences and the data accumulated.

The written guidelines gave the interviews a framework and generated topics of conversation. Unfortunately, they also restricted conversation. Anxious to address all the listed topics, the participants and I tended to adhere closely to the protocol instead of exploring more pertinent personal issues. In a future project, an open interview technique may be more beneficial.

Notwithstanding the problems encountered in the formal interviews, the conversations were beneficial.

Interviewing – the therapeutic effect

Talking about a crisis experience is known to facilitate a cathartic release of emotional tension. Moreover, when a person reflects on an experience or situation, talking through it helps him to piece together the fragments of the experience, facilitating understanding and personal growth. Essentially, therefore, conversation allows an increase in self-awareness.

Certainly, several participants acknowledged the benefits of talking. For example, at the end of his fourth formal interview, Dave made the following comment:

> *Talking to you enables me to sort out my own thoughts.... It crystallises my thoughts. Sometimes, when my mind is in a muddle, I can't think. I don't know what I'm thinking. To be able to talk to somebody, like we're talking now, helps me to sort out my thoughts.... I mean, some of the things that we're talking about now, I wasn't even aware of. They were subconscious thoughts that have become conscious thoughts....*

Similarly, Bill highlighted the importance of simply talking as he lamented his inability to communicate with a young woman who was dying:

> *She was a frightened woman, very frightened. It's a pity that there wasn't somebody in the family, somebody like yourself, that could talk to 'er, but I found that I couldn't go in the room.... I could talk to 'er 'usband, but all I could say to 'er was 'And 'ow's Lorraine today?'*

In contrast, Richard discovered that talking stirred up painful memories and uncovered old forgotten fears. At the end of his second

10. DISCUSSION AND CONCLUSIONS

interview, he realised that he would have to take sleeping tablets that night, because he'd be thinking about everything he'd been saying that afternoon.

Throughout the project, I was concerned about the duration of the interviews and their impact on the participants. The participants, however, said that they appreciated the opportunity of talking to someone who understood their situation and who wasn't directly involved in it. They also commented that the interviews served as a bridge, allowing them to 'keep in touch' with the outside world. Moreover, they confirmed the value of the interviews in subtle ways, either by asking me when the next meeting would occur or by continuing interviews beyond the allotted timespan.

Written accounts

Diary accounts and written briefs were two rich sources of data. Each allowed a unique insight into the experience of illness. In the diary accounts, the participants kept a record of their thoughts and experiences. These accounts were pure, lived experiences rather than remembered impressions that had undergone interpretation. Moreover, the accounts were accurate as they were unaffected by the participants' memory loss. In contrast, the written briefs provided a retrospective report on the illness experience. Obviously, the participants' perceptions of their past experiences altered with time; therefore, the reports contained an element of bias. Nevertheless, the written briefs were important in that they allowed the participants an opportunity to explore, evaluate and then capture their whole illness experience in writing.

Ethical considerations reviewed

At the outset of the project, I was aware of the many potential ethical problems associated with an investigation involving people with acute leukaemia. Nevertheless, in retrospect, I was very naive regarding the effect of the research activities both on myself and the participants. From the participants' perspective, the data collection represented an invasion of privacy, while the writing process caused problems with confidentiality and exploitation (Munhall 1988). Exploitation occurred as I interpreted and described the patients' perceptions and experiences of illness. For, in explaining the data, I assumed a knowledge of the participants' thoughts and feelings. Cottle (1977) argues that the intense investigator–participant relationship allows the investigator to know the participants and, through this knowledge, he earns the right to speak for the participants. From my perspective, the research method had an emotional cost.

In choosing to explore the experience of leukaemia, I encountered and became involved with people in crisis. In order to cope with the emotional stresses associated with the intense personal involvement, I adopted various coping strategies.

Perhaps my most important coping strategy was my debriefing system. I established a network of trusted nursing colleagues, family members and friends, one of whom was available to me after a formal interview or a period of ward work. These meetings provided me with an emotional outlet and helped to alleviate my burden of involvement. Times of escape also helped. The days away from the project enabled me to separate myself from the participants and the stresses associated with their world.

As I collected and collated the data, I took time to reflect on my experiences and feelings. Recording careful descriptions of the research encounters helped me to monitor and control my personal involvement in the project. Later, as I read through these descriptions, I gained a deeper understanding of the participants and their world. Additionally, my understanding of the illness setting, its impact on myself and the participants also developed. Gradually, I became more sensitive towards the participants and their situation, and this sensitivity enhanced the ongoing process of interviewing and writing. Finally, the descriptions added meaning to the work for, as Cottle (1974, p.145) contends, 'The expression of the investigator's feelings, moreover, contributes to the reality of the situation, for the situation is in part composed of the investigator.'

Section III: Limitations of the study

This book describes the illness experience of a comparatively small number of patients and it may not therefore be representative of the leukaemia population in general. The project was also of comparatively short duration and, consequently, the accounts do not refer to some of the long-term effects of illness. Moreover, the participants had a common cultural background and their ages covered a relatively narrow range.

Despite these shortcomings, the eight portraits of illness do offer a different perspective on leukaemia and provide a new insight into the illness passage. They reveal a need to assess and change certain aspects of practice. In addition, although the vignettes only explore a single disease process, there is great variation in the individual accounts. Certainly, the illness career of each participant varies in timespan and outcome. Additionally, the information gleaned from the vignettes can also be applied to patients with other types of ailment. Indeed the attitudes, feelings and experiences displayed by the eight participants are relevant to patients with a variety of malignant and even benign conditions.

Future work

Age, social class and gender are all significant factors in the illness experience (Lipowski 1969). Future studies could, therefore, investigate the experiences of adolescent or elderly individuals with leukaemia and the effects of gender and/or social class on the individual's response to illness. Knowledge from these works would provide a more complete picture of the leukaemia experience.

Illness is recognised as being 'culture-dependent'. Hence, a future, parallel work could look at the illness experience in a contrasting cultural setting. The findings from this study would aid our understanding of illness by identifying how cultural beliefs and values influence the individual's perception and response to illness.

Illness with leukaemia was seen to have a profound and long-lasting impact upon close family members, particularly the spouse. Further work is needed to explore the spouse's and the other family members' perceptions of illness and to identify the factors that influence their ability to cope. The observations from this study would enhance our comprehension of the family's illness experience and would facilitate more effective and appropriate nursing intervention.

Accordingly, illness has a profound effect upon professional caregivers. Due to the intense, long-term nature of the disease, nursing and medical staff may develop an intimate relationship with the patient and his family members. Before professional staff are able to minister to the needs of the family in crisis, they must understand their own reactions to the experience of illness and suffering. Therefore, another study could explore the impact of the illness experience upon professional staff who are working in the acute illness setting.

The experience of long-term illness is not unique to patients with leukaemia. Consequently, it would be interesting to explore the illness experience in contrasting disease processes such as diabetes, chronic heart disease or rheumatoid arthritis. The findings of these comparative and complementary studies would enhance our understanding of the illness experience in general and would establish the criteria for appropriate nursing intervention and patient support in the broader context of illness.

Section IV: Implications for nursing education

The portraits of illness identify various issues that relate to nursing education. Firstly, to ensure a firm basis for practice where care reflects the meanings and concerns of each individual in a unique way, nursing education needs to encompass a philosophy of care and provide a theoretical understanding of man and his beliefs (Granstrom 1985, Griffin 1980). Secondly, in order to execute optimal physical and emotional care to individuals with leukaemia and other forms of life-threatening illness, nurses require an understanding of the disease process and the treatment rationale. Furthermore, knowledge of cognitive and behavioural coping strategies and comprehension of the illness experience may help them to understand and interpret the person's response to illness. Thirdly, it is essential that nurses learn to 'listen' to patients, and that they develop communication and basic counselling skills within the confines of the therapeutic relationship.

In a list of recommendations to care-givers, Jeremy addressed the practicalities of how to institute a counselling programme:

> There could be a case (on an entirely voluntary basis) for senior, more mature nurses to have a counselling module available in their training. The actual time spent in counselling would be recorded in the notes and in most cases the patient would be unaware of this difference in approach. Counselling, when done properly, is not a mentally draining activity.

Quoting the results of several recent studies, Corner (1989) describes

10. DISCUSSION AND CONCLUSIONS

how nurses hold negative and stereotyped attitudes to cancer. These attitudes stem from inadequate preparation during nurse training and subsequently affect the quality of care that cancer patients receive. To overcome their fears, nurses need to see patients as unique and interesting individuals rather than as disease labels. In addition, they need to see the potential of the illness experience and not merely the limitations of disease. By providing an illustration of the leukaemia experience, this book provides knowledge to further the understanding of leukaemia and gives insight into the meaning of illness and the person's response to illness. It is hoped that, if this text is used for teaching purposes, it will help nurses to overcome their fears of caring for patients with life-threatening disease and will expand the enjoyment that they find in their work.

Summary

Caring for the patient with leukaemia is not an easy task. The physical, emotional, social, sexual and spiritual impact of the disease is enormous. Consequently, care must be highly skilled and appropriate to the needs of the patient as he progresses through illness.

The personal stories of the eight participants in this book illustrate the long-term experience of illness. They demonstrate the effects of acute myeloid leukaemia and show how it influences every area of a person's life. By examining the patients' perspective of illness, insight is gained into the disease process and the physical effects of infirmity are discovered. In particular, the portraits uncover the reality of alienation and the loss of identity associated with diagnosis. Then, as the person progresses through the illness passage, the personal accounts reveal the stigma and the uncertainty that accompany daily life. They show the impact of long-term hospitalisation, the value of privacy, the importance of regular visitors and the need to promote autonomy by allowing patients a measure of responsibility in decision-making and care. Finally, the portraits reveal the significance of ongoing counselling support for patients and their family members.

Despite the knowledge and insight gleaned from this study, the patient is still the 'expert' authority on his illness. It is only by knowing the patient throughout his illness that the nurse learns to interpret and understand his intentions and behaviours and that she comprehends his experience of illness. In order to understand a patient's experiences and provide appropriate care, the nurse must listen to and learn from the patient. She must get to know the patient's own changing story. She must know how he understands the symptoms of his disease and how illness has disrupted his daily life. Essentially, she must learn to see the patient in his own context; she must see the reality of his world.

References

Aamodt AM 1986 Discovering the child's view of alopecia: doing ethnography. In: Munhall P, Oiler C (ed) Nursing research: a qualitative approach. Appleton Century Crofts, New York, ch. 9.

Almquist G et al 1986 Pediatric bone marrow transplantation: developing a patient education booklet. Journal of the Association of Pediatric Oncology Nurses 3 (1): 13–18

Bellert JH 1989 Humor: a therapeutic approach in oncology nursing. Cancer Nursing 12 (2): 65–70

Burnard P 1989 Counselling skills for health professionals. Chapman & Hall, London

Corner JL 1988 Assessment of nurses' attitudes towards cancer: a critical review of research methods. Journal of Advanced Nursing 13: 640–648

Cottle TJ 1974 Black children, white dreams. Houghton Mifflin, Boston

Cottle TJ 1977 Private lives and public accounts. University of Massachusetts Press, Amherst, MA

Cousins N 1979 Anatomy of an illness (as perceived by the patient). WS Norton, New York

Cousins N 1982 The physician as communicator. JAMA 248 (5): 587–589

Field PA, Morse JM 1985 Nursing research: the application of qualitative approaches. Croom Helm, Beckenham, Kent

Granstrom SL 1985 Spiritual nursing care for oncology patients. Topics in Clinical Nursing April: 39–45

Griffin AP 1988 Philosophy and nursing. Journal of Advanced Nursing 5: 261–272

Herth K 1990 Contributions of humor as perceived by the terminally ill. American Journal of Hospice Care Jan–Feb: 36–40

Holcombe A 1987 Bone marrow harvest. Oncology Nursing Forum Mar–Apr 14 (2): 63-65

Holland J 1977 Psychological aspects of oncology. Medical Clinics of North America 61(4): 737–748

Howser DM 1987 Hickman catheter care: developing organised teaching strategies. Cancer Nursing 10 (2): 70–76

Lipowski ZJ 1969 Psychosocial aspects of disease. Annals of Internal Medicine 71: 1197–1206

Munhall PL 1988 Ethical considerations in qualitative research. Western Journal of Nursing Research April 10 (2): 150–162

O'Rourke A 1986 Bone marrow procedure guide. Oncology Nursing Forum 13 (1): 66–67

Rowden L 1984 Relaxation and visualisation: techniques in patients with breast cancer. Nursing Times 12 Sep: 42–45

Simonton C, Mathews-Simonton S, Creighton J 1978 Getting well again. Bantam Books, London

Snyder JC, Wilson MF 1977 Elements of psychological assessment. American Journal of Nursing Feb: 235–237

Stedeford A 1983 The dying patient and his family. Medical Education International 1610–1613

Travelbee J 1971 Interpersonal aspects of nursing, 2nd edn. FA Davies, Philadelphia

Watson PM 1982 Patient education: the adult patient with cancer. Nursing Clinics of North America 17 (4): 739–752

Watson PG 1990 Review – Cancer rehabilitation: the evolution of a concept. Cancer Nursing Feb 13 (1): 2–12